Learning About Informed Consent, Capacity Assessments, Treatment Refusal, Civil Commitment, and Boundary Violations

A Programmed Text

Theodore A. Stern, MD

Ronald Schouten, MD, JD

Learning About Informed Consent, Capacity Assessments, Treatment Refusal, Civil Commitment, and Boundary Violations

A Programmed Text

Learning About Informed Consent, Capacity Assessments, Treatment Refusal, Civil Commitment, and Boundary Violations: A Programmed Text

ISBN-13: 978-1-951166-97-7 (print)
ISBN-13: 978-1-951166-96-0 (ebook)

Book Production: Dianne Russell, Octal Productions, LLC
Copyeditor: Bob Russell, Octal Publishing, LLC
Cover Design: Falcone Creative Design, LLC
Book Design: Dianne Russell, Octal Productions, LLC
Printing and Binding: RP Graphics
Production Managers: Jane Pimental and Grace Shanks, MGH Psychiatry Academy
This book is printed on acid-free paper.

To lifelong learners across multiple disciplines.

Table of Contents

Preface

Learning about informed consent, competency, treatment refusal, civil commitment, malpractice, and boundary violations, as well as the role of psychiatrists in the legal system will help to frame the practice of clinicians and facilitate ethical and effective care.

To assess your knowledge about this subject, a pre-test is provided.

After taking this pre-test, move directly to the text (**without checking the answer key** at the end of the book).

Next, read the programmed text. It provides you with an opportunity for layered learning, with information offered in bite-sized bits. After each section, fill in the missing words (indicated by blanks) with the correct answer; this enables you to build knowledge in small steps. You will learn better if you do not look at the answers before you fill in the missing words. Therefore, cover up the answer adjacent to each section using the supplied *bookmark* (found at the back of this book), until you have filled in the missing words.

This format makes this volume appear incredibly simple; nevertheless, completing this step-by-step workbook will help you to achieve a working knowledge about informed consent, competency, treatment refusal, civil commitment, malpractice, and boundary violations. Follow the instructions; skipping sections will interfere with the learning process. You can complete the tests and read the text in one sitting.

After completing the entire text, take the post-reading test. This helps you to assess how much you have learned from this exercise.

Then, score your pre-test and post-reading test to determine your raw score and percentage of correct responses so that you can see how much you have learned.

Enjoy the painless process.

Theodore A. Stern, MD
Ronald Schouten, MD, JD

Pre-Reading Quiz

Pre-Reading Quiz: Answer Sheet

1. _____

2. _____

3. _____

4. _____

5. _____

6. _____

7. _____

8. _____

9. _____

10. _____

11. _____

12. _____

13. _____

14. _____

15. _____

16. _____

17. _____

18. _____

19. _____

20. _____

21. _____

22. _____

23. _____

24. _____

25. _____

26. _____

27. _____

28. _____

29. _____

30. _____

31. _____

32. _____

33. _____

34. _____

35. _____

36. _____

37. _____

38. _____

39. _____

40. _____

41. _____

42. _____

43. _____

44. _____

45. _____

46. _____

47. _____

48. _____

49. _____

50. _____

Pre-Reading Quiz: Questions

1. Which of the following is at the core of the Anglo-American legal system?
   A. Case law
   B. Civil law
   C. Criminal law
   D. Malpractice law

2. Which type of law is predominantly based on statutes enacted by legislatures?
   A. Case law
   B. Civil law
   C. Criminal law
   D. Malpractice law

3. Which of the following types of law is a subset of tort law?
   A. Civil law
   B. Criminal law
   C. Malpractice law
   D. Tax law

4. Which of the following, if absent, can lead to a victim suing for damages stemming from unpermitted touching?
   A. Consent
   B. Payment
   C. Pleasure
   D. Witnesses

5. Which of the following is the term used when a failure to act would likely lead to an imminent, serious, and negative effect on a patient's condition?

A. An emergency

B. A futile situation

C. As soon as possible (ASAP)

D. An urgent situation

6. Which of the following terms is described by "consent given after a sharing of knowledge and a chance to consider alternative options"?

A. Capacity

B. Informed consent

C. Simple consent

D. The professional standard

7. Which of the following (in addition to having the appropriate information and competency) is a legal requirement for informed consent?

A. Absence of an emergency

B. Absence of psychosis

C. The ability to speak

D. Voluntariness

8. When a clinician provides the amount of information that an average patient would require to make a decision under the same circumstances, it is said to meet which of the following conditions?

A. Competency

B. Simple consent

C. The materiality standard

D. The professional standard

9. For a patient to give informed consent, he or she must have which of the following?

    A. A desire to improve

    B. A high school education

    C. Less than 6 out of 10 on the pain scale

    D. The capacity to make informed decisions

10. True or False. The capacity to accept a procedure is the same as it is to refuse a procedure.

    A. True

    B. False

11. Which of the following terms used by courts strips a person of certain rights and privileges normally accorded to adults?

    A. Delirium

    B. Dementia

    C. Incompetence

    D. Schizophrenia

12. After a psychiatrist determines that a patient lacks the capacity to refuse a non-emergent procedure, the treating team should do which of the following?

    A. Administer an antipsychotic agent to enhance cooperation

    B. Seek out an alternative decision-maker

    C. Treat the patient as he or she would any patient with that condition

    D. Withhold the treatment refused by the patient

13. Which of the following terms denotes the capacity to serve as a witness in court?

    A. Global capacity

    B. Professional capacity

    C. Testamentary capacity

    D. Testimonial capacity

14. Which of the following pairs of authors created the standard approach to the assessment of decision-making capacity?
    A. Appelbaum and Grisso
    B. Hackett and Cassem
    C. Kahana and Bibring
    D. Stanton and Schwartz

15. Which of the following is a key component of the capacity assessment?
    A. Determining whether the patient agrees with the recommendations of the provider
    B. Determining whether the patient can pay for the services recommended
    C. Determining whether the patient has had a similar procedure before
    D. Determining whether the patient has a factual understanding of the information provided

16. True or False. A person can be deemed competent to make their own treatment decisions but still be unable to manage their financial affairs.
    A. True
    B. False

17. Which of the following is an exception to obtaining fully informed consent?
    A. An acute psychotic illness
    B. A disagreement with the treating physician
    C. An emergency
    D. A terminal illness

18. True or False. All competent people have a right to make their own medical treatment decisions, even when the individual is suffering from a serious mental illness or is civilly committed.
    A. True
    B. False

19. True or False. The standard of proof is lower for civil commitment cases than it is for ordinary civil cases and for criminal cases.

A. True

B. False

20. Which of the following is the standard of proof needed for criminal cases?

A. A lack of remorse for the crime

B. Beyond a reasonable doubt

C. Clear and convincing evidence

D. Eye-witness testimony

21. Criteria for civil commitment can include which of the following?

1. Dangerousness to self as evidenced by threats or attempts to cause self-harm

2. Dangerousness to others as evidenced by threats or attempts to cause harm

3. Dangerousness to self as evidenced by inability to provide for oneself

4. Inability to make informed decisions regarding treatment of one's mental illness

A. 1 & 2

B. 2 & 4

C. 1, 2, & 3

D. All of the above

22. Exceptions to informed consent include which of the following?

1. Emergency

2. Incompetence

3. Waiver

4. Patient would be dissuaded from making the right decision

A. 1 & 2

B. 2 & 4

C. 1, 2, & 3

D. All of the above

23. Which of the following is the standard of proof to be considered competent to stand trial?
    A. Ability to understand the charges against one
    B. Beyond a reasonable doubt
    C. Preponderance of the evidence
    D. Scoring ≥ 26 on the Mini-Mental State Examination

24. Which of the following is the focus of competency evaluations to stand trial?
    A. The defendant's mental state at the time of the alleged act
    B. The defendant's mental state at the time of the proceedings
    C. The defendant's educational history
    D. The defendant's history of a psychotic illness

25. True or False. The defendant's consent is not necessary for a competency evaluation; the court can order it over the defendant's objection.
    A. True
    B. False

26. True or False. The Eighth Amendment prohibits execution of incompetent mentally ill prisoners as cruel and unusual punishment.
    A. True
    B. False

27. True or False. For an act to be criminal, there must be both a guilty act (the *actus reus*) and guilty intent (*mens rea*); that is, the mental state required as an element of a specific crime.
    A. True
    B. False

28. True or False. Mental illness caused by substance abuse, exacerbation of an existing mental illness due to intoxication, and pathologic intoxication does not provide a basis for an insanity defense.
    A. True
    B. False

29. Which of the following has served as the basis for the legal standards of the insanity defense?
    A. Atkins test
    B. M'Naghten test
    C. Penry test
    D. Roper test

30. Which of the following is a cognitive test, focusing only on whether the defendant knew what he was doing or that what he was doing was wrong?
    A. Atkins test
    B. M'Naghten test
    C. Penry test
    D. Roper test

31. Which of the following is the usual disposition when a defendant is found not guilty by reason of insanity?
    A. A correctional facility
    B. A freestanding psychiatric hospital
    C. A general hospital
    D. Their home

32. Which of the following is a defense that can be raised where an individual suffers from a mental illness or cognitive deficit that does not meet the requirements of the insanity defense, but nevertheless provides a basis for not holding the person fully responsible for the behavior?
    A. Antisocial personality
    B. Diminished capacity
    C. Incompetence
    D. Voluntary intoxication

33. In what percentage of cases is the insanity defense raised in felony trials?

    A.   0.1%

    B.   1%

    C.   5%

    D.   10%

34. True or False. Juries hand down 5% of insanity acquittals, whereas 40% to 50% are decided by judges; the remainder are a result of plea bargains.

    A.   True

    B.   False

35. In which of the following situations do psychiatrists who work within general hospitals typically first become involved with the legal system?

    A.   When a psychiatrist receives a subpoena for medical records

    B.   When a psychiatrist is asked to determine whether an individual is competent to stand trial

    C.   When a psychiatrist is asked to determine if an individual has the capacity to make a will

    D.   When a psychiatrist is asked to determine if an individual qualifies for an insanity defense

36. True or False: The forensic evaluator's primary obligation is to the individual being evaluated.

    A.   True

    B.   False

37. True or False. There is no doctor-patient relationship in a forensic evaluation.

    A.   True

    B.   False

38. True or False. Confidentiality is limited in a forensic evaluation because it is being conducted on behalf of a third party who has requested the evaluation.

A. True

B. False

39. Which of the following is the term used to describe a witness who has knowledge related to the subject matter of the litigation beyond that of the average juror or judge, and who can offer information that will be useful to the judge or jury in reaching a decision in the matter?

A. Credible witness

B. Expert witness

C. Fact witness

D. Officer of the court

40. Which of the following terms is used to describe an individual who has firsthand knowledge related to the matter being decided?

A. Credible witness

B. Expert witness

C. Fact witness

D. Officer of the court

41. The reasons for requiring that the defendant be competent to stand trial during criminal proceedings include:

1. It makes the trial go faster.

2. It preserves the integrity of the legal system.

3. It makes the defense attorney's job easier.

4. It helps to ensure a fair trial.

A. 1 & 3

B. 2 & 4

C. 1, 2, & 3

D. All of the above

42. True statements about the psychotherapist-patient privilege include:

1. Unlike confidentiality, the patient must raise the privilege to keep the physician from testifying.

2. A treating clinician might be required to testify concerning otherwise-confidential information about his or her patient if the patient asks the clinician to do so (express waiver).

3. A treating clinician might be required to testify concerning otherwise-confidential information about his or her patient if the patient has put his mental state in issue as part of the legal proceedings (implied waiver).

4. The treating clinician believes it is in the patient's best interests.

   A. 1 & 2

   B. 2 & 4

   C. 1, 2, & 3

   D. All of the above

43. Which of the following are elements of a malpractice claim?

1. Departure from the standard of care

2. Existence of a duty of care

3. Direct or proximate causation

4. Damages

   A. 1 & 3

   B. 2 & 4

   C. 1, 2, & 3

   D. All of the above

44. Sexual relations with a patient can result in which of the following?

1. Suspension or loss of the psychiatrist's medical license

2. Ethical censure

3. A malpractice claim

4. Criminal conviction

   A. 1 & 3

   B. 2 & 4

   C. 1, 2, & 3

   D. All of the above

45. True or False. Dereliction of duty can be established either by showing that the treating clinician departed from (or ignored) the standard of care or by establishing that the treating clinician followed the standard of care but did so in an inept fashion.

   A. True

   B. False

46. True or False. The general duty of physicians is to possess and employ such reasonable skill and care as are commonly had and are exercised by respectable, average physicians in the same or similar community.

   A. True

   B. False

47. True or False. A physician who holds him or herself out as an expert in a specific area will be judged according to this higher standard, regardless of the actual credentials.

   A. True

   B. False

48. True or False. In a malpractice case, the plaintiff does not need to prove that there are damages; it is sufficient to show that there was a negligent performance of a duty.

   A. True

   B. False

49. True or False. Abandonment, in malpractice cases, can be either intentional (e.g., the doctor decides that he or she no longer wants to see a patient), or unintentional (e.g., while planning to do so, the doctor forgets to arrange for cover during vacation).

   A. True

   B. False

50. True or False. Abandonment is defined as the unilateral termination of the doctor-patient relationship, by the patient, without consent or justification, in which the termination results in harm to the patient.

   A. True

   B. False

Cover the answers as you take the pre-test by using the bookmark (shown here) found at the back of this book.

# Time to Begin

Remember to fill in the missing words (indicated by the blank spaces) before you look at the answers (i.e., in the shaded area adjacent to the text).

Enjoy the process.

Informed Consent, Capacity Assessment, Treatment Refusal, and Civil Commitment, and Boundary Violations

Overview

- Informed consent and civil commitment are concepts that are essential to the treatment of patients who suffer from mental illness.
- Just as in the rest of medicine, patients with mental illness are presumed to be competent and to have a right to make their own treatment decisions. This includes informed consent, a process in which the treating clinician describes the proposed treatment and its risks and benefits, and the patient has an opportunity to ask questions and to make the final decision.
- Civil commitment is a legal process that allows the state to deprive a person of certain liberty interests (e.g., the right to move freely in the community) if that person poses a danger to themselves or others due to mental illness.

Theoretical Basis

- Informed consent represents an ethical obligation to respect the autonomy interests of individual patients, enforced by case law and statutes.
- Civil commitment proceedings are governed by the need to protect constitutional rights.

Clinical Applications

- Informed consent applies in all clinical interactions. There are exceptions to it, however, such as emergencies, waiver, incompetence, and therapeutic privilege.
- Civil commitment is a formal process that allows a person to be confined to a mental health facility for evaluation and treatment if that person refuses voluntary admission and is deemed to represent a danger to themselves or others.

Important Historical Proponents

- The ethical basis of informed consent arises from libertarian philosophers like John Stuart Mill, who emphasized the importance and benefits of allowing individuals to make their own life choices.
- The law of informed consent is based in the ancient tort of trespass or battery: the touching of another person without consent or justification could be the basis of a suit for monetary damages.
- Informed consent in medicine as a legal requirement was developed in the United States in the mid-twentieth century.

Overview

Psychiatrists, more so than those in any other medical specialty, interact with the legal system on a regular basis.

_____, *more so than those in any other med-*   Psychiatrists
ical specialty, interact with the legal system on a reg-
ular basis.

Issues related to informed consent, competency to consent to treatment, treatment refusal, and civil commitments are important aspects of daily clinical practice. These four topics are reviewed in this chapter.

Issues related to informed consent, competency to consent to treatment, treatment refusal, and civil commitments are important aspects of daily _____ *practice.*

clinical

They are just four of the topics belonging to the subspecialty of *forensic psychiatry*, which focuses on the application of clinical principles and practice to the legal system.

They are just four of the topics belonging to the subspecialty of _____ *psychiatry, which focuses on the application of clinical principles and practice to the* _____ *system.*

forensic

legal

The core of the Anglo-American legal system is case law, also known as common law or judge-made law, to reflect the fact that the legal principles are developed through decisions in cases that address similar legal issues.

The core of the Anglo-American legal system is _____ *law, also known as common* _____ *or judge-made law, to reflect the fact that the legal principles are developed through decisions in* _____ *that address similar legal issues.*

case

law

cases

A substantial portion of civil law is case-based, whereas most of the criminal law is based on statutes enacted by legislatures. The four topics addressed in this section belong to the realm of the civil law.

A substantial portion of _____ *law is case-based, whereas most of the* _____ *law is based on statutes enacted by legislatures. The four topics addressed in this section belong to the realm of the civil law.*

civil
criminal

A major component of civil law is personal injury or *tort law*. A tort is a civil wrong that gives rise to a right to sue for damages; in other words, A injures B, either intentionally or negligently, which gives B the right to sue A for compensation for the damages that occurred.

A major component of civil law is _____ *injury or* tort _____. *A* _____ *is a civil wrong that gives rise to a right to* _____ *for damages; in other words, A injures B, either intentionally or negligently, which gives B the right to sue A for compensation for the* _____ *that occurred.*

personal
law; tort
sue

damages

Informed Consent

Relevance

One of the earliest principles of tort law prohibited the touching of another person unless consent had been obtained or there was some justification.

One of the earliest principles of tort law prohibited the touching of another person unless _____ *had been obtained or there was some justification.*

consent

In the absence of consent or justification, the unpermitted touching constitutes the civil wrong or tort of battery and gives the victim the right to sue for damages.

In the absence of _____ or justification, the `consent`
unpermitted touching constitutes the civil wrong or
_____ of battery and gives the victim the right `tort`
to _____ for damages. `sue`

Consent to being touched can be express (the patient explicitly consenting to treatment) or implied (e.g., a patient standing in a clearly marked line to receive an inoculation).

Consent to being touched can be _____ `express`
(the patient explicitly consenting to treatment) or
_____ (e.g., a patient standing in a clearly `implied`
marked line to receive an inoculation).

Justification occurs when there is an emergency; that is, failure to act would likely have an imminent, serious negative effect on the patient's condition.

Justification occurs when there is an _____; `emergency`
that is, failure to act would likely have an imminent,
serious negative effect on the patient's condition.

Initially, simple consent was sufficient: the person being touched need only give a general consent to the touching, without any further explanation.

Initially, simple consent was sufficient: the person
being touched need only give a general _____ `consent`
to the touching, without any further explanation.

The notion of *informed consent*—consent given after a sharing of knowledge and a chance to consider alternative options—existed only as an ethical concept until it was adopted by one of the American courts beginning in the 1960s and it began to be converted to a legal duty on the part of physicians.

The notion of _____ consent—consent given *after a sharing of knowledge and a chance to consider alternative options—existed only as an ethical concept until it was adopted by one of the American courts beginning in the 1960s and it began to be converted to a legal _____ on the part of physicians.*

informed

duty

From a clinical and ethical standpoint, informed consent arises from the physician's obligation to respect the autonomy of the patient.

From a clinical and ethical standpoint, informed consent arises from the physician's obligation to respect the _____ of the patient.

autonomy

Case law, and in many jurisdictions, statutes, require that clinicians obtain informed consent before providing treatment, unless one of the exceptions to informed consent applies.

Case law, and in many jurisdictions, statutes, require that clinicians obtain informed _____ before providing treatment, unless one of the _____ to informed consent applies.

consent
exceptions

Lack of informed consent is a basis for alleging medical malpractice.

Lack of _____ consent is a basis for alleging medical _____.

informed
malpractice

Defining Informed Consent

Informed consent is a process through which the physician obtains the permission of the patient or a substitute decision maker to provide treatment to the patient.

Informed consent is a _____ through which the physician obtains the permission of the patient or a substitute decision maker to provide _____ to the patient.

process

treatment

The decision maker must be *competent* (i.e., have the capacity to make the decision), must be given enough *information* to make an informed decision, and must make the decision *voluntarily.*

The decision maker must be _____ (i.e., have the capacity to make the decision), must be given enough _____ to make an informed decision, and must make the decision _____.

competent

information
voluntarily

The legal requirements of informed consent are likewise information, competency, and voluntariness.

The _____ requirements of informed consent are likewise _____, competency, and voluntariness.

legal
information

Information

The amount and type of information that must be given to the patient to meet the requirements of informed consent varies among jurisdictions.

The amount and type of _____ that must be given to the patient to meet the requirements of informed consent varies among _____.

information

jurisdictions

Three basic standards (i.e., the professional standard, the materiality standard, and the combined standard) are used in this area.

Three basic standards (i.e., the _____ stan-dard, the _____ standard, and the combined standard) are used in this area.

With the *professional* standard, the clinician is expected to provide information to the same extent that a reasonable professional would do so under similar circumstances.

With the _____ standard, the clinician is expected to provide information to the same extent that a reasonable professional would do so under similar circumstances.

With the *materiality* standard, the clinician must provide the degree of information that the average patient would require to make a decision under the same circumstances. This is also referred to as a *patient-oriented* standard. In some jurisdictions (e.g., Massachusetts), the concept is extended to require provision of the information that would be material to the specific patient's decision.

With the _____ standard, the clinician must provide the degree of information that the average _____ would require to make a decision under the same circumstances. This is also referred to as a _____-oriented standard. In some jurisdictions (e.g., Massachusetts), the concept is extended to require provision of the information that would be material to the specific patient's decision.

With the combined standard, the clinician should provide the information that the reasonable medical practitioner would provide but also examine whether it was "sufficient to insure informed consent."

professional
materiality

professional

materiality

patient

patient-

With the _____ standard, the clinician should provide the information that the reasonable medical practitioner would provide but also examine whether it was "sufficient to insure informed consent."

combined

Providing the following information to patients will fulfill the information requirements in most jurisdictions: the nature of the condition to be treated and the treatment proposed; the nature and probability of the risks associated with the treatment (minor risks or side effects that occur frequently [e.g., dry mouth] and significant risks that occur infrequently [e.g., hepatic failure secondary to sodium valproate]) should be reviewed with the patient; the inability to predict the results of the treatment; the irreversibility of the procedure, if applicable; and, the alternative treatments available, including no treatment.

Providing the following information to patients will fulfill the information requirements in most jurisdictions: the nature of the _____ to be treated and the _____ proposed; the nature and probability of the _____ associated with the treatment (minor risks or side effects that occur _____ [e.g., dry mouth] and significant risks that occur _____ [e.g., hepatic failure secondary to sodium valproate]) should be reviewed with the patient; the inability to predict the results of the treatment; the irreversibility of the procedure, if applicable; and, the _____ treatments available, including no treatment.

condition
treatment
risks

frequently
infrequently

alternative

Competency

For a patient to give adequate informed consent, he or she must have the physical and mental capacity to make informed treatment decisions.

For a patient to give adequate _____ con-sent, he or she must have the physical and mental _____ to make informed treatment decisions.

informed

capacity

How much capacity is required depends upon the nature of the condition and the risks of the proposed treatment.

How much _____ is required depends upon the nature of the condition and the risks of the pro-posed _____.

capacity

treatment

Less capacity is required for low-risk treatments with a high likelihood of a good result (e.g., intravenous flu-ids for rehydration).

Less capacity is required for _____-risk treat-ments with a high likelihood of a good result (e.g., intravenous fluids for rehydration).

low-

A higher level of capacity is required when the treat-ment is of higher risk or is more invasive, and the results are less likely to be favorable (e.g., aortic valve replacement in an 84-year-old patient with dementia).

A higher level of capacity is required when the treat-ment is of _____ risk or is more invasive, and the results are _____ likely to be favor-able (e.g., aortic valve replacement in an 84-year-old patient with dementia).

higher

less

Technically, competency is a legal, rather than clinical, concept.

Technically, competency is a _____, rather than clinical, concept.

legal

In the eyes of the law, all adults are presumed to be competent to make their own treatment decisions, and only a court of law can declare someone legally incompetent.

In the eyes of the law, all adults are presumed to be _____ to make their own treatment decisions, and only a court of law can declare someone legally _____.

competent

incompetent

A legal declaration of incompetence strips a person of certain rights and privileges normally accorded to adults; for example, making treatment decisions, making contracts, voting, or executing a will.

A legal declaration of _____ strips a person of certain rights and privileges normally accorded to adults; for example, making treatment decisions, making contracts, voting, or executing a will.

incompetence

A clinician who opines that a patient is "incompetent" to make treatment decisions has no authority to declare the person incompetent in a legal sense; however, that opinion will be considered if a court is asked to consider the matter.

A clinician who opines that a patient is "_____" to make treatment decisions has no authority to declare the person incompetent in a legal sense; however, that opinion will be considered if a court is asked to consider the matter.

incompetent

There is a trend in the law for courts to use the term "capacity" rather than "competency" to be more specific in identifying what abilities the person in question possesses or lacks.

There is a trend in the law for courts to use the term "_____" rather than "_____" to be more specific in identifying what abilities the person in question possesses or lacks.

Although they do not alter a patient's legal status, clinical assessments of capacity (still commonly referred to as competency evaluations) are the first step toward a legal declaration of incompetence, and they often predict the likely outcome of any legal proceedings.

Although they do not alter a patient's legal status, clinical assessments of _____ (still commonly referred to as _____ evaluations) are the first step toward a legal declaration of _____, and they often predict the likely outcome of any _____ proceedings.

In the face of doubts about a patient's mental status, treatment will generally proceed if there is a clinical determination that a patient has adequate decision-making capacity. On the other hand, a conclusion that the patient lacks the capacity to give informed consent generally requires that an alternative decision maker be found.

In the face of doubts about a patient's mental status, treatment will generally proceed if there is a clinical determination that a patient has adequate _____-making capacity. On the other hand, a conclusion that the patient lacks the _____ to give informed consent generally requires that an alternative decision maker be found.

Ideally, this decision maker will have been previously appointed by the patient through a valid advance directive.

Ideally, this decision maker will have been previously appointed by the patient through a valid _____ directive.

advance

Short of going to court for a formal declaration of incompetence and judicial appointment of a guardian, decisions are often made on behalf of the incompetent patient by family members or others who can utilize a *substituted judgment analysis* to reach a treatment decision that the patient would have made if competent.

Short of going to court for a formal declaration of _____ and judicial appointment of a _____, decisions are often made on behalf of the incompetent patient by family members or others who can utilize a substituted _____ analysis to reach a treatment decision that the patient would have made if competent.

incompetence
guardian

judgment

All adults are presumed to be competent under the law. That is, they are assumed to have the capacity to engage in the full range of activities and responsibilities commensurate with independent adult life.

All adults are presumed to be _____ under the law. That is, they are assumed to have the _____ to engage in the full range of activities and responsibilities commensurate with independent adult life.

competent

capacity

A declaration of incompetence (incapacity) can be global or task specific. *Global incapacity* refers to the inability to undertake and to carry out any of the normal responsibilities and rights of an adult.

A declaration of _____ *(incapacity) can be* *global or task* _____. Global incapacity *refers* *to the inability to undertake and to carry out any of* *the normal responsibilities and rights of an adult.*

incompetence
specific

A declaration of global incompetence by a court strips an individual of his or her rights as a legal person. As a result, courts prefer to declare people incompetent regarding specific capacities, preserving as much of their autonomy as possible.

A declaration of _____ *incompetence by* *a court strips an individual of his or her rights as a* *legal person. As a result, courts prefer to declare peo-* *ple incompetent regarding specific* _____, *pre-* *serving as much of their autonomy as possible.*

global

capacities

The following are examples of specific capacities (e.g., testamentary capacity, testimonial capacity).

The following are examples of specific _____ *(e.g., testamentary capacity, testimonial capacity).*

capacities

Testamentary capacity is the capacity to execute a will. Specific legal standards for testamentary capacity apply in all jurisdictions and can vary.

Testamentary capacity *is the capacity to execute a* _____. *Specific legal standards for testamen-* *tary capacity apply in all jurisdictions and can vary.*

will

The usual standards require that the person executing the will know the nature of the document being executed; know the general contents of the estate; and know the persons who would normally inherit from him or her (the natural objects of his or her bounty).

The usual standards require that the person executing the will know the nature of the document being executed; know the general contents of the _____ ; estate *and know the persons who would normally _____ from him or her (the natural objects of* inherit *his or her bounty).*

Testimonial capacity is the capacity to serve as a witness in court.

Testimonial capacity is the capacity to serve as a _____ in court. witness

Assessing Capacity to Make Treatment Decisions

The process of assessing a patient's capacity to make treatment decisions focuses on his or her ability to understand and to process relevant information. A standard approach to assessing decision-making capacity was described by Appelbaum and Grisso in 1988.

The process of assessing a patient's _____ capacity *to make treatment decisions focuses on his or her _____ to understand and to process relevant information. A standard approach to assessing decision-making capacity was described by Appelbaum and Grisso in 1988.* ability

When evaluating the capacity to make treatment decisions, Appelbaum and Grisso suggested asking the following questions: Does the patient express a preference? Is the patient able to attain a factual understanding of the information provided? Is the patient able to appreciate the seriousness of the condition and the consequences of accepting or rejecting treatment? Can the patient manipulate the information provided in a rational fashion and come to a decision that follows logically from that information considered in the context of the individual's personal beliefs, experience, and circumstances?

When evaluating the capacity to make treatment decisions, Appelbaum and Grisso suggested asking the following questions: Does the patient express a _____? Is the patient able to attain a _____ understanding of the information provided? Is the patient able to _____ the seriousness of the condition and the consequences of accepting or rejecting treatment? Can the patient _____ the information provided in a rational fashion and come to a decision that follows _____ from that information considered in the context of the individual's personal beliefs, experience, and circumstances?

preference
factual
appreciate

manipulate

logically

It is the process of reaching a decision, not the decision itself, that must be rational.

It is the _____ of reaching a decision, not the _____ itself, that must be rational.

process
decision

Competent people have a right to make decisions for themselves that might seem irrational to the rest of the world.

Competent people have a right to make decisions for themselves that might seem _____ to the rest of the world.

irrational

Disagreement with the treating clinician's recommendations is not a basis in and of itself for saying that a patient is irrational.

_____ with the treating clinician's recommendations is not a basis in and of itself for saying that a patient is irrational.

Disagreement

Consequences of a Finding of Incapacity

After a patient has been assessed as lacking capacity to make treatment decisions, there are several possible options, depending upon the nature of the condition and the law in that jurisdiction.

After a patient has been assessed as lacking _____ to make treatment decisions, there are several possible options, depending upon the nature of the condition and the _____ in that jurisdiction.

capacity

law

Guardianship of the Person

A traditional model under these circumstances is for the court to appoint a *guardian of the person.*

A traditional model under these circumstances is for the court to appoint a _____ of the person.

guardian

The person declared incompetent is the *ward*, and the *guardian* is any person appointed by the court to make decisions on behalf of the ward.

The person declared incompetent is the _____,   ward
and the _____ is any person appointed by the   guardian
court to make decisions on behalf of the ward.

The term "incapacitated person" is beginning to replace "ward" in many legal jurisdictions, although "ward" is still used commonly.

The term "_____ person" is beginning to   incapacitated
replace "ward" in many legal jurisdictions, although
"ward" is still used commonly.

Depending upon the jurisdiction, the guardian might make decisions based upon the perceived best interests of the ward or by means of a *substituted judgment analysis* (what the individual would have decided if he or she were competent to make the decision).

Depending upon the jurisdiction, the _____   guardian
might make decisions based upon the perceived
_____ interests of the ward or by means of a   best
_____ judgment analysis (what the individual   substituted
would have decided if he or she were competent to
make the decision).

In cases involving extraordinary or invasive treatment, many states require that the substituted judgment analysis be carried out by a judge rather than by the guardian.

In cases involving extraordinary or invasive treatment,
many states require that the _____ judgment   substituted
analysis be carried out by a _____ rather than   judge
by the guardian.

Guardianship of the Estate (Conservatorship)

This involves the appointment of an agent to act on behalf of the person deemed incompetent to manage financial matters. A person can be deemed competent to make their own treatment decisions but still be unable to manage their financial affairs.

This involves the appointment of an _____ to act on behalf of the person deemed _____ to manage with financial matters. A person can be deemed competent to make their own treatment decisions but still be unable to manage their _____ affairs.

agent
incompetent

financial

Voluntary

As one of the three elements of informed consent, voluntary simply means free of coercion by those proposing the treatment.

As one of the three elements of informed consent, _____ means free of coercion by those proposing the treatment.

voluntary

Persuasion by family members does not void informed consent so long as the circumstances do not put the physician on notice that the treatment is being imposed against the patient's specific wishes or to take advantage of the patient or indicate that the patient is incompetent.

_____ by family members does not void informed consent so long as the circumstances do not put the physician on notice that the treatment is being imposed against the patient's specific wishes or to take advantage of the patient or indicate that the patient is incompetent.

Persuasion

Exceptions to the Requirement of Informed Consent

There are several situations in which the obligation to obtain fully informed consent is suspended. These can include emergency situations, waivers to informed consent, and therapeutic privilege.

There are several situations in which the obligation to obtain fully informed _____ is suspended. These can include _____ situations, _____ to informed consent, and therapeutic _____.

consent
emergency
waivers
privilege

An emergency is defined as a situation in which failure to act would result in a serious and imminent deterioration in the patient's condition. The emergency exception allows for initiation of treatment and stabilization, not for ongoing treatment without obtaining proper consent.

An _____ is defined as a situation in which failure to act would result in a serious and imminent deterioration in the patient's condition. The emergency exception allows for _____ of treatment and stabilization, not for ongoing treatment without obtaining proper consent.

emergency

initiation

For situations in which a patient has previously informed his or her physician about treatment preferences in the event of an emergency, the physician is generally held to have an obligation to comply with those instructions.

For situations in which a patient has previously informed his or her physician about treatment _____ in the event of an emergency, the physician is generally held to have an _____ to comply with those instructions.

preferences
obligation

A patient can make an informed decision to defer to someone else's judgment regarding treatment decisions, including the treating clinician's judgment. A waiver can be implied; for example, presenting oneself to the emergency room after being injured. Or it can be explicit; for example, "Please don't tell me anymore; you just do what's best."

A patient can make an informed decision to _____ to someone else's judgment regarding treatment decisions, including the treating clinician's judgment. A _____ can be _____; for example, presenting oneself to the emergency room after being injured. Or it can be _____; for example, "Please don't tell me anymore; you just do what's best."

defer

waiver; implied

explicit

The patient must have the capacity to waive informed consent, which means that they must at least be aware of the nature of the condition, the level of risk involved in the treatment, that they or someone else they choose has a right to decide, and that they are waiving that right.

The patient must have the _____ to waive informed consent, which means that they must at least be aware of the nature of the condition, the level of risk involved in the treatment, that they or someone else they choose has a right to decide, and that they are _____ that right.

capacity

waiving

Therapeutic privilege applies in those relatively rare circumstances in which the process of providing information and obtaining consent would result in a serious risk of deterioration in the patient's condition.

_____ privilege applies in those relatively rare circumstances in which the process of providing information and obtaining consent would result in a serious risk of _____ in the patient's condition.

Therapeutic

deterioration

In those situations, the informed consent process can be deferred until the patient's condition has improved sufficiently. The possibility that providing the information might lead to treatment refusal is not sufficient to invoke therapeutic privilege.

In those situations, the informed consent process can be _____ until the patient's condition has improved sufficiently. The possibility that providing the _____ might lead to treatment refusal is not sufficient to invoke therapeutic privilege.

deferred

information

Treatment Refusal

All competent people have a right to make their own medical treatment decisions, and all adults are presumed to be competent. This applies even where the individual is suffering from serious mental illness or is civilly committed.

All _____ people have a right to make their own medical treatment decisions, and all _____ are presumed to be competent. This applies even where the individual is suffering from serious mental illness or is civilly committed.

competent
adults

The presumption of competency persists until a court has declared a person to be incompetent.

The presumption of competency persists until a _____ has declared a person to be incompetent.

court

When a patient is believed to be incapacitated and unable to make treatment decisions, an alternative decision maker should be sought rather than relying on the presumption of competence and allowing the patient to continue making treatment decisions.

When a patient is believed to be incapacitated and unable to make treatment _____, an alternative _____ maker should be sought rather than relying on the presumption of competence and allowing the patient to continue making treatment decisions.

decisions
decision

Individuals who are incompetent still have a right to individual autonomy, which can be honored by following their preferences for treatment expressed when they were competent or to the extent they can be determined in the absence of prior expression.

Individuals who are incompetent still have a right to individual _____, which can be honored by following their preferences for treatment expressed when they were _____ or to the extent they can be determined in the absence of prior expression.

autonomy

competent

The law concerning treatment refusal varies among the states. States generally draw a distinction between routine and ordinary medical care, (e.g., antibiotics, minor surgery), and extraordinary or invasive care (e.g., cancer chemotherapy, coronary artery bypass grafting) when determining what can be done when a patient refuses treatment.

The law concerning treatment refusal varies among the states. States generally draw a distinction between _____ and ordinary medical care, (e.g., antibiotics, minor surgery), and extraordinary or _____ care (e.g., cancer chemotherapy, coronary artery bypass grafting) when determining what can be done when a patient refuses treatment.

routine

invasive

Benzodiazepines and antidepressants are generally considered to be routine, ordinary, and non-invasive.

Benzodiazepines and antidepressants are generally considered to be _____, ordinary, and non-invasive.

routine

Antipsychotic medication, electroconvulsive therapy, and psychosurgery are considered to constitute extraordinary, dangerous, and invasive treatments in many states.

_____ medication, _____ therapy, and psychosurgery are considered to constitute extraordinary, dangerous, and _____ treatments in many states.

Antipsychotic; electroconvulsive

invasive

States differ in terms of what legal steps must be taken before a patient's refusal of treatment can be overridden. The basic rule in all states is that competent individuals have a right to make their own treatment decisions, including refusal of treatment that others believe is in the patient's best interest.

States differ in terms of what legal steps must be taken before a patient's _____ of treatment can be overridden. The basic rule in all states is that _____ individuals have a right to make their own treatment decisions, including refusal of treatment that others believe is in the patient's best _____.

refusal

competent

interest

Exceptions to this rule exist in matters involving criminal law and the correctional system.

Exceptions to this rule exist in matters involving _____ law and the correctional system.

criminal

When a patient who appears to lack the capacity to make treatment decisions refuses routine and ordinary care, physicians can generally rely upon family members or significant others who know the patient to decide.

When a patient who appears to lack the _____ *to make treatment decisions refuses routine and* _____ *care, physicians can generally rely upon family members or significant others who know the patient to decide.*

capacity

ordinary

When the care to be provided is extraordinary, invasive, or dangerous, many states require that a formal guardian be appointed to make the treatment decisions.

When the care to be provided is extraordinary, _____, *or dangerous, many states require that a formal* _____ *be appointed to make the treatment decisions.*

invasive

guardian

Guardianship is established after a hearing at which family members, treaters, and sometimes the patient, will testify.

Guardianship is established after a _____ *at which family members, treaters, and sometimes the patient, will* _____.

hearing

testify

Not all states allow the guardian, after having been appointed, to make all decisions on behalf of the patient. In some states, only a judge can authorize extraordinary, invasive, or dangerous treatment and only after a full adversarial hearing on the issue (*Rogers v. Commissioner* [Mass. 1983]).

Not all states allow the _____, after having been appointed, to make all decisions on behalf of the patient. In some states, only a _____ can authorize _____, invasive, or dangerous treatment and only after a full adversarial hearing on the issue (Rogers v. Commissioner *[Mass. 1983]*).

guardian

judge
extraordinary

However, others (including Federal courts) hold that professional judgment and administrative review satisfy the due process requirements without going to court (*Rennie v. Klein* [3rd Circuit 1981]); *U.S. v. Charters* [4th Circuit 1988]).

However, others (including Federal courts) hold that professional judgment and administrative review satisfy the _____ process requirements without going to court (Rennie v. Klein *[3rd Circuit 1981]); U.S. v.* Charters *[4th Circuit 1988]*).

due

Refusal of treatment by those awaiting trial or those already convicted of a crime has been the subject of considerable judicial attention.

Refusal of _____ by those awaiting trial or those already convicted of a _____ has been the subject of considerable judicial attention.

treatment
crime

Antipsychotic medications may be administered over the refusal of convicted prisoners, competent or incompetent, if an independent review panel agrees that the prisoner suffers from a serious mental illness, is dangerous to himself or others, or is gravely disabled and the medication proposed is in the prisoner's best interests (*Washington v. Harper* [U.S. 1990]).

_____ medications may be administered over the refusal of convicted prisoners, competent or incompetent, if an independent review panel agrees that the prisoner suffers from a serious _____ illness, is dangerous to himself or others, or is gravely disabled and the medication proposed is in the prisoner's best interests (Washington v. Harper [U.S. 1990]).

Antipsychotic

mental

Forced administration of antipsychotic medication to render the inmate competent to be executed raises significant ethical issues for psychiatrists as well as important questions of constitutional law. Some states consider this permissible, whereas others hold that doing so violates constitutional principles (such as the right to privacy) and constitutes cruel, excessive, and unusual punishment (*Louisiana v. Perry* [La. 1992]). The American Medical Association takes the position that it is unethical for physicians to treat death row inmates for the purpose of restoring them to competency to be executed.

Forced administration of antipsychotic medication to render the inmate _____ to be executed raises significant ethical issues for psychiatrists, as well as important questions of constitutional law. Some states consider this permissible, while others hold that doing so violates constitutional principles (such as the right to privacy) and constitutes cruel, excessive, and unusual _____ (Louisiana v. Perry [La. 1992]). The American Medical Association takes the position that it is unethical for physicians to treat death row inmates for the purpose of restoring them to competency to be executed.

competent

punishment

Forced administration of antipsychotic medication to render a defendant competent to stand trial violated the rights of the defendant under the Sixth and Fourteenth Amendments to the United States Constitution absent a showing by the state that the treatment was both medically necessary and appropriate and furthers a compelling governmental interest (*Riggins v. Nevada* [U.S. 1992]; *Sell v. United States* [U.S. 2003]).

Forced administration of _____ *medication to render a defendant* _____ *to stand trial violated the rights of the defendant under the Sixth and Fourteenth Amendments to the United States Constitution absent a showing by the state that the treatment was both medically necessary and appropriate and furthers a compelling governmental interest* (Riggins v. Nevada *[U.S. 1992]*; Sell v. United States *[U.S. 2003]*).

antipsychotic
competent

Civil Commitment

The process of hospitalizing a person against his or her will is referred to as *involuntary civil commitment*.

The process of hospitalizing a person against his or her will is referred to as _____ *civil commitment.*

involuntary

Civil commitment statutes are similar in the various jurisdictions, as all states provide for commitment when a person poses a danger to himself or herself or others.

Civil _____ *statutes are similar in the various jurisdictions, as all states provide for commitment when a person poses a* _____ *to himself or herself or others.*

commitment

danger

Confinement of an individual by the state against his or her will is a deprivation of fundamental rights guaranteed under the Constitution of the United States and state constitutions, unless specific legal requirements are met. Some states also require that the person being committed lacks the capacity to make decisions regarding his or her own treatment.

Confinement of an individual by the state against his or her _____ is a deprivation of fundamental rights guaranteed under the _____ of the United States and state constitutions, unless specific legal requirements are met. Some states also require that the person being committed lacks the _____ to make decisions regarding his or her own treatment.

will
Constitution

capacity

Civil commitment is an act of the government because it occurs under the authority of state or federal law.

Civil _____ is an act of the government because it occurs under the authority of state or federal law.

commitment

The United States Supreme Court has held that commitment to a mental hospital entails a curtailment of liberty interests and requires due-process protection (*Vitek v. Jones*, 445 U.S. 480 [U.S. 1980]). Before the government can deprive someone of their fundamental rights, proper procedural protections (e.g., a court or administrative hearing before a neutral fact-finder) must be granted. Such procedures collectively constitute procedural due process, which is guaranteed by the Constitution.

The United States Supreme Court has held that commitment to a mental hospital entails a curtailment of liberty interests and requires due-_____ protection (Vitek v. Jones, 445 U.S. 480 [U.S. 1980]). Before the government can deprive someone of their fundamental _____, proper procedural protections (e.g., a court or administrative hearing before a neutral fact-finder) must be granted. Such procedures collectively constitute procedural due process, which is guaranteed by the _____.

process

rights

Constitution

Lawsuits for deprivation of civil rights, false imprisonment, and negligence can arise from improper civil commitment.

Lawsuits for deprivation of civil rights, false imprisonment, and negligence can arise from improper _____ commitment.

civil

A person can be involuntarily committed only if that person is a danger to himself or herself or others, either by threats or attempts to cause harm, or being unable to provide for oneself in the community.

A person can be _____ committed only if that person is a danger to _____ or _____ or others, either by threats or attempts to cause harm, or being unable to provide for oneself in the community.

involuntarily
himself; herself

The fact that a patient might demonstrate a clear-cut clinical need for treatment, in the absence of dangerousness, is not sufficient. The United States Supreme Court has held that a state cannot constitutionally confine a non-dangerous individual who is capable of surviving outside the hospital setting on his own or with the help of friends (*O'Connor v. Donaldson* [U.S. 1974]).

The fact that a patient might demonstrate a clear-cut clinical need for treatment, in the absence of _____, is not sufficient. The United States Supreme Court has held that a state cannot constitutionally confine a non-_____ individual who is capable of surviving outside the hospital setting on his own or with the help of friends (O'Connor v. Donaldson *[U.S. 1974]*).

dangerousness

dangerous

The minimal standard of proof in all civil commitment cases is "clear and convincing" evidence: more than is required in ordinary civil cases and less than this is needed in the criminal standard of beyond a reasonable doubt (*Addington v. Texas* [U.S. 1979]). Individual states might provide additional protections, by requiring proof beyond a reasonable doubt for civil commitment.

*The minimal standard of proof in all _____ commitment cases is "clear and convincing" _____: more than is required in ordinary civil cases and less than this is needed in the criminal standard of beyond a reasonable _____ (*Addington v. Texas *[U.S. 1979]). Individual states might provide additional protections, by requiring proof beyond a reasonable doubt for civil commitment.*

civil

evidence

doubt

However, the details of the commitment process vary among the states. States also differ in how mental illness is defined. Some states, for example, do not consider substance abuse and disorders like Alzheimer's disease as mental illnesses for civil commitment to a psychiatric hospital, but they might allow involuntary confinement to other facilities that specialize in treatment of those conditions.

However, the details of the commitment process vary among the states. States also differ in how mental illness is defined. Some states, for example, do not consider substance abuse and disorders like Alzheimer's disease as mental illnesses for _____ commitment to a psychiatric hospital, but they might may allow involuntary confinement to other facilities that specialize in treatment of those conditions.

civil

For circumstances in which a patient is offered an opportunity to sign himself into a state hospital voluntarily and does so while lacking the capacity to make an informed decision, he has been deprived of his Constitutional right to due process of law, and the state and its agents can be held liable for a violation of the patient's federal civil rights (*Zinermon v. Burch* [U.S. 1990]).

For circumstances in which a patient is offered an opportunity to sign himself into a state hospital _____ and does so while lacking the _____ to make an informed decision, he has been deprived of his Constitutional right to due process of law, and the state and its agents can be held _____ for a violation of the patient's federal civil rights (Zinermon v. Burch [U.S. 1990]).

voluntarily
capacity

liable

Although the details differ, all states use the criteria of danger to self or others as the basis for involuntary commitment. The danger must be the result of mental illness rather than ordinary anger or antisocial behavior.

Although the details differ, all states use the criteria of _____ to self or others as the basis for _____ commitment. The danger must be the result of mental illness rather than ordinary anger or antisocial behavior.

danger
involuntary

For example, a hired killer would not be an appropriate candidate for involuntary commitment to a psychiatric hospital should his murderous intentions become known, absent evidence that a mental illness contributed to his dangerousness.

For example, a hired killer would not be an appropriate candidate for _____ commitment to a psychiatric hospital should his murderous intentions become known, absent evidence that a _____ illness contributed to his dangerousness.

involuntary

mental

However, an individual convicted of a violent crime can be committed to a hospital if it is determined that he poses a danger to himself or others.

However, an individual convicted of a violent crime can be committed to a hospital if it is determined that he poses a _____ to himself or others.

danger

Danger to self means attempts at serious self-harm or suicide, or credible threats to cause such self-harm.

Danger to self means attempts at serious _____- harm or suicide, or credible threats to cause such self-harm.

self-

Danger to others generally refers to threats or attempts to cause physical harm to others, or actual harm already inflicted. In addition, it can include situations in which others are placed in reasonable fear that they will be harmed by the patient.

Danger to _____ generally refers to threats or attempts to cause physical harm to others, or actual harm already inflicted. In addition, it can include situations in which _____ are placed in reasonable fear that they will be harmed by the patient.

others

others

Individuals can also be involuntarily committed if they pose a substantial risk of harm because they are unable to provide for their own well-being in the community. In some states, this criterion is referred to as the *gravely disabled* criterion.

Individuals can also be _____ *committed if they pose a substantial risk of harm because they are unable to provide for their own well-being in the community. In some states, this criterion is referred to as the* gravely _____ *criterion.*

involuntarily

disabled

Generally, mere difficulty caring for oneself is not enough to fulfill this criterion. The risk of harm—for example, believing that one is invincible and therefore can walk into traffic—must be substantial and imminent. A likelihood of harm in the distant future is not sufficient. Civil commitment under this criterion, as well as the others, is permissible only if no less restrictive alternative is available in the community (*Lake v. Cameron* [D.C. Cir. 1966]).

Generally, mere difficulty _____ *for one-self is not enough to fulfill this criterion. The risk of* _____—*for example, believing that one is invincible and therefore can walk into traffic—must be substantial and* _____. *A likelihood of harm in the distant future is not sufficient. Civil commitment under this criterion, as well as the others, is permissible only if no less* _____ *alternative is available in the community (*Lake v. Cameron *[D.C. Cir. 1966]).*

caring

harm

imminent

restrictive

Alternatives to civil commitment can include increased outpatient visits, voluntary hospitalization, day hospital programs, custodial care by relatives, or shelters.

Alternatives to civil _____ can include increased outpatient visits, voluntary hospitalization, day hospital programs, custodial care by relatives, or shelters.

commitment

Civil commitment of criminal defendants and convicted individuals has been the subject of important court decisions. The due process clause requires that the reason for confinement and the nature of the confinement be reasonably related to the purpose of confinement.

Civil commitment of criminal defendants and convicted individuals has been the subject of important court decisions. The due _____ clause requires that the reason for confinement and the nature of the confinement be reasonably related to the purpose of confinement.

process

For example, in *Jackson v. Indiana* (U.S. 1972), Jackson was deaf, with limited ability to sign, and had limited intellectual ability. He had been found incompetent to stand trial on charges of shoplifting and was committed to the state hospital until he was restored to competency, which everyone agreed was unattainable under the circumstances. The Supreme Court held that if the state wanted to continue to confine Jackson to a mental institution, he must meet standard criteria for civil commitment.

For example, in Jackson v. Indiana (U.S. 1972), Jackson was deaf, with limited ability to sign, and had limited intellectual ability. He had been found incompetent to stand trial on charges of shoplifting and was committed to the state hospital until he was restored to competency, which everyone agreed was unattainable under the circumstances. The Supreme Court held that if the state wanted to continue to confine Jackson to a mental institution, he must meet standard criteria for civil _____.

commitment

Individuals found not guilty by reason of mental illness (insanity acquittees) may be confined to psychiatric hospitals as long as they are mentally ill and dangerous, but no longer. As the Supreme Court held in *Jones v. United States* (U.S. 1983):

> "...the Constitution permits the Government, on the basis of the insanity judgment, to confine (a defendant) to a mental institution until such time as he has regained his sanity or is no longer a danger to himself or society. This holding accords with the widely and reasonably held view that insanity acquitees should not be treated differently from other candidates for civil commitment." (*Jones v. United States*, 463 U.S. 354 [1983])

Individuals found not _____ *by reason of*   guilty
mental illness (insanity acquittees) may be confined
to psychiatric hospitals as long as they are mentally
ill and _____, *but no longer. As the Supreme*   dangerous
Court held in Jones v. United States *(U.S. 1983):*

> *"...the Constitution permits the Government, on the basis of the insanity judgment, to confine (a defendant) to a mental institution until such time as he has regained his sanity or is no longer a danger to himself or society. This holding accords with the widely and reasonably held view that insanity acquitees should not be treated differently from other candidates for civil commitment." (*Jones v. United States, 463 U.S. 354 [1983])*

The Supreme Court has held that a state statute violated the Due Process Clause of the United States Constitution where it allowed a criminal defendant who was found not guilty by reason of insanity to be returned to the hospital, even if a hospital review committee found him no longer mentally ill, if he was determined at a court hearing to be dangerous (*Foucha v. Louisiana* [U.S. 1992]).

The Supreme Court has held that a state statute violated the Due _____ *Clause of the United*   Process
States Constitution where it allowed a criminal defendant who was found not guilty by reason of _____ *to be returned to the hospital, even if a*   insanity
*hospital review committee found him no longer mentally ill, if he was determined at a court hearing to be dangerous (*Foucha v. Louisiana *[U.S. 1992]).*

The hospital psychiatrist testified that Foucha had recovered from the drug-induced psychosis that was the basis for his insanity defense, but also testified that Foucha had been in altercations at the hospital, had an antisocial personality disorder that was not a mental disease and was untreatable, and the psychiatrist would not "feel comfortable in certifying that he would not be a danger to himself or to other people."

The hospital psychiatrist testified that Foucha had recovered from the drug-induced psychosis that was the basis for his _____ *defense, but also testi-*   insanity
fied that Foucha had been in altercations at the hospital, had an antisocial personality disorder that was not a mental disease and was untreatable, and the psychiatrist would not "feel comfortable in certifying that he would not be a danger to himself or to other people."

The Court held that continued confinement in a mental institution is improper without a determination in civil commitment proceedings of current mental illness and dangerousness. The state's legitimate interest in imprisoning convicted criminals for retribution and deterrence does not exist in the case of an insanity acquittee, who has not been found guilty and cannot be punished.

The Court held that continued _____ in a mental institution is improper without a determination in civil _____ proceedings of current mental illness and dangerousness. The state's legitimate interest in imprisoning convicted criminals for retribution and deterrence does not exist in the case of an insanity acquittee, who has not been found guilty and cannot be punished.

confinement

commitment

The Supreme Court has also held that a state may legitimately detain people who are unable to control their behavior and thereby pose a danger to public safety, provided the confinement takes place pursuant to proper procedures and evidentiary standards.

The Supreme Court has also held that a state may legitimately detain people who are unable to control their _____ and thereby pose a _____ to public safety, provided the confinement takes place pursuant to proper procedures and evidentiary standards.

behavior; danger

For example, it held that Kansas' *Sexually Dangerous Predator Act* is not unconstitutional where it establishes procedures for the civil commitment of persons who, due to a "mental abnormality" or "personality disorder" are likely to engage in "predatory acts of sexual violence" (*Hendricks v. Kansas* [U.S. 1997]).

For example, it held that Kansas' Sexually Dangerous Predator Act *is not unconstitutional where it establishes procedures for the civil* _____ *of persons who, due to a "mental abnormality" or "personality disorder" are likely to engage in "predatory acts of sexual violence"* (Hendricks v. Kansas [U.S. 1997]).

commitment

Involuntary civil confinement, which follows conclusion of criminal sentence if the individual is found to be a sexually dangerous person, did not constitute additional punishment for criminal behavior, because it does not have the primary goals of retribution or deterrence.

Involuntary _____ *confinement, which follows conclusion of criminal sentence if the individual is found to be a sexually dangerous person, did not constitute additional punishment for criminal behavior, because it does not have the primary goals of retribution or deterrence.*

civil

Procedures provided by the state, including the right to immediate release when the detainee proves he or she is no longer sexually dangerous, are adequate.

Procedures provided by the _____, *including the right to immediate release when the detainee proves he or she is no longer sexually dangerous, are adequate.*

state

Criminal Issues and the Role of Psychiatrists in the Legal System

Overview

- Most treating clinicians encounter the criminal justice system only in those infrequent instances when a patient finds himself or herself charged with a criminal violation.
- A defendant's mental state plays a key role relative to the core concepts of the criminal justice system: competence to stand trial and criminal responsibility.

Theoretical Basis

- A defendant must be competent to stand trial before he or she can be tried and either acquitted or convicted.
- To be considered competent to stand trial, the defendant must have sufficient present ability to consult with his lawyer with a reasonable degree of rational understanding, and a rational as well as a factual understanding of the charges against him.
- Society provides that people who commit crimes may be relieved of criminal responsibility if they suffer from a mental disease or defect and are determined to meet the criteria for the insanity defense in the jurisdiction where they are being tried. There are two basic types of insanity defense criteria.
- One requires that the defendant suffer from a mental disease or defect that prevents them from appreciating the wrongfulness of their conduct at the time of the crime. This is often referred to as the right–wrong test.
- The second type also uses the right–wrong test, but adds an alternative criterion: the defendant lacked substantial capacity to conform his behavior to the requirements of the law. This latter aspect, standing alone, is referred to as the irresistible impulse test.

Clinical Applications

- Treating psychiatrists should not offer opinions about their patients' competency to stand trial or criminal responsibility. Those evaluations and opinions should be left to independent, objective forensic experts.
- However, the treating psychiatrist should cooperate with the forensic evaluator if the patient–defendant waives confidentiality.

Important Historical Proponents

- The concept of an insanity defense has been known to multiple cultures for centuries. Competency to stand trial is a more recent development and had its origins in the English common law.

Overview

Psychiatrists play an important role in the courts as evaluators, consultants, and expert witnesses in civil and criminal litigation. This section focuses on criminal competencies, criminal responsibility, the psychotherapist–patient privilege, and the role of the psychiatrist in court.

Competency in the Criminal System

The question of a defendant's competency arises regarding several different steps in the criminal justice process. The most common is competency to stand trial.

The question of a defendant's competency arises regarding several different steps in the _____ justice process. The most common is competency to stand _____.

criminal

trial

The basic standard for competency to stand trial is whether the defendant "has sufficient present ability to consult with his lawyer with a reasonable degree of rational understanding, and whether he has a rational as well as a factual understanding of the proceedings against him" (*Dusky v. U.S.* [U.S. 1960]). This standard applies in all states, the District of Columbia, and federal courts. States may use their own criteria, so long as they provide as much, or more, protection of the defendant's rights as the federal standard.

The basic standard for competency to stand _____ is whether the defendant "has sufficient present ability to consult with his _____ with a reasonable degree of rational understanding, and whether he has a rational as well as a factual _____ of the proceedings against him" (Dusky v. U.S. *[U.S. 1960]). This standard applies in all _____, the District of Columbia, and federal courts. States may use their own criteria, so long as they provide as much, or _____, protection of the defendant's rights as the federal standard.*

trial
lawyer

understanding

states

more

Because it is so important that the defendant be competent to stand trial, the standard of proof for incompetence is "preponderance of the evidence"; that is, the judge must be convinced that it is more likely than not that the defendant is incompetent. (*Cooper v. Oklahoma* [U.S., 1996]).

Because it is so important that the defendant be _____ to stand trial, the standard of proof for incompetence is "preponderance of the _____"; that is, the judge must be convinced that it is more likely than not that the defendant is incompetent. (Cooper v. Oklahoma *[U.S., 1996]).*

competent
evidence

Nevertheless, in practice the threshold for competency is generally low; for instance, the defendant will usually be found competent to stand trial if he or she meets the most minimal capacity requirements.

Nevertheless, in practice the threshold for competency is generally _____; for instance, the defendant will usually be found competent to stand trial if he or she meets the most minimal _____ requirements.

low

capacity

The emphasis on a defendant being competent to stand trial is the result of several important principles (*Drope v. Missouri* [U.S. 1975]). These include: the fact-finding portion of the proceedings can be accurate only if the defendant can work with his or her attorney with an understanding of the proceedings; only a competent defendant can exercise the Constitutional rights to a fair trial and to confront his or her accuser in a meaningful way; the integrity and dignity of the legal process are preserved and the purposes of retribution and individual deterrence are served only if the convicted defendant is competent to stand trial.

The emphasis on a defendant being _____ to stand trial is the result of several important principles (Drope v. Missouri [U.S. 1975]). These include: the fact-finding portion of the proceedings can be accurate only if the defendant can work with his or her attorney with an _____ of the proceedings; only a competent defendant can exercise the _____ rights to a fair trial and to confront his or her accuser in a meaningful way; the integrity and dignity of the legal process are preserved and the purposes of retribution and individual deterrence are served only if the convicted defendant is competent to stand _____.

competent

understanding
Constitutional

trial

Evaluation of Competency to Stand Trial

The focus of the competency evaluation is the defendant's mental state at the time of the proceedings, not at the time of the alleged criminal act.

The focus of the competency evaluation is the defendant's mental _____ at the time of the _____, not at the time of the alleged _____ act.

state; proceedings
criminal

A defendant's competency can fluctuate over the course of the proceedings, and the question of a defendant's competency to stand trial can be raised at any point during those proceedings and by any of the key participants: defense counsel, the prosecution, or the judge.

A defendant's _____ can fluctuate over the course of the proceedings, and the question of a defendant's competency to stand trial can be raised at any point during those proceedings and by any of the key participants: defense counsel, the prosecution, or the _____.

competency

judge

When there is evidence of a lack of competency, the judge has an obligation to raise the question if the defense and prosecution fail to do so (*Pate v. Robinson* [U.S. 1966]).

When there is evidence of a lack of competency, the _____ has an obligation to raise the question if the defense and prosecution fail to do so (Pate v. Robinson [U.S. 1966]).

judge

After it is determined that an evaluation is necessary, the judge can order that it take place. The evaluation can be done on an outpatient basis, but it is more commonly conducted on an inpatient unit with special capabilities to conduct forensic evaluations.

After it is determined that an evaluation is necessary, the _____ can order that it take place. The evaluation can be done on an outpatient basis, but it is more commonly conducted on an inpatient unit with special capabilities to conduct _____ evaluations.

judge

forensic

The defendant's consent is not necessary for a competency evaluation; the court can order it over the defendant's objection (*U.S. v. Hugenin* [1st Cir. 1991]). Under the Sixth Amendment, the defendant has a right to consult with his or her attorney before the competency evaluation, but in federal courts, the defendant has no right to have counsel present at the evaluation itself. States may provide this right, if they choose (*Buchanan v. Kentucky* [U.S. 1987]).

The defendant's consent is not necessary for a _____ evaluation; the court can order it over the defendant's objection (U.S. v. Hugenin [1st Cir. 1991]). Under the Sixth Amendment, the defendant has a right to consult with his or her _____ before the competency evaluation, but in _____ courts, the defendant has no right to have counsel present at the evaluation itself. States may provide this right, if they choose (Buchanan v. Kentucky [U.S. 1987]).

competency

attorney
federal

The decision as to whether the defendant is competent to stand trial is made by the trial judge.

The decision as to whether the defendant is _____ to stand trial is made by the trial _____.

competent
judge

If the defendant is found to be incompetent to stand trial, he or she is committed to a state or federal hospital to be treated and restored to competency.

If the defendant is found to be incompetent to stand trial, he or she is _____ to a state or federal hospital to be treated and restored to competency.

committed

Restoration to competency can occur on an outpatient basis, but this is less common. If the defendant cannot be restored to competency, he or she cannot be convicted and must be released from the hospital. However, the defendant can be held in the facility if he or she meets the usual criteria for civil commitment (*Jackson v. Indiana* [U.S. 1972]).

Restoration to competency can occur on an outpatient basis, but this is less common. If the defendant cannot be restored to _____, he or she cannot be _____ and must be released from the hospital. However, the defendant can be held in the facility if he or she meets the usual criteria for civil _____ (Jackson v. Indiana [U.S. 1972]).

competency
convicted

commitment

Forced administration of antipsychotic medication to render a defendant competent to stand trial violated the rights of the defendant under the Sixth and Fourteenth Amendments to the U.S. Constitution, absent a showing by the state that the treatment was both medically necessary and appropriate and furthers a compelling governmental interest (*Riggins v. Nevada* [U.S. 1992]; *Sell v. United States* [U.S. 2003]).

Forced administration of antipsychotic medication to render a defendant _____ to stand trial violated the rights of the defendant under the Sixth and Fourteenth Amendments to the U.S. Constitution, absent a showing by the state that the treatment was both medically necessary and appropriate and furthers a compelling governmental interest (Riggins v. Nevada [U.S. 1992]; Sell v. United States [U.S. 2003]).

competent

Competency to Waive the Right to Counsel/Represent Oneself

Defendants have a constitutional right to have legal representation, and in felony cases are entitled to have legal representation provided by the government if they cannot afford it. Defendants also have the right to represent themselves and to waive the right to counsel; however, they must be deemed competent to do so.

_____ *have a constitutional right to have legal representation, and in felony cases are entitled to have legal representation provided by the government if they cannot afford it. Defendants also have the right to represent themselves and to waive the right to counsel; however, they must be deemed* _____ *to do so.*

Defendants

competent

The Supreme Court has held that the standard for competency to waive this right is no higher than that for competency to stand trial, and essentially requires that the waiver must be knowing and voluntary. (*Godinez v. Moran* [509 U.S. 389, 1993]). In *Indiana v. Edwards* [554 U.S. 164, 2008] the Supreme Court held that the right to self-representation is not absolute, that a defendant may be competent to stand trial but not to serve as his own attorney, and that the state may require such a defendant to proceed to trial with counsel.

The Supreme Court has held that the standard for competency to waive this right is no higher than that for _____ *to stand trial, and essentially requires that the waiver must be knowing and voluntary. (Godinez v. Moran [509 U.S. 389, 1993]). In* Indiana v. Edwards *[554 U.S. 164, 2008] the Supreme Court held that the right to self-representation is not absolute, that a defendant may be competent to stand trial but not to serve as his own attorney, and that the state may require such a defendant to proceed to trial with counsel.*

competency

Competency to Be Sentenced or Executed

The Supreme Court has held that execution of a prisoner who is incompetent constitutes cruel and unusual punishment in violation of the Eighth Amendment to the Constitution (*Ford v. Wainwright* [U.S.1986]).

The Supreme Court has held that _____ of a prisoner who is incompetent constitutes cruel and unusual _____ in violation of the Eighth Amendment to the Constitution (Ford v. Wainwright [U.S.1986]).

execution

punishment

The standard for competency to be sentenced or executed is virtually identical to that for competency to stand trial: Whether the convicted individual understands the nature of the proceedings and an ability to participate in the process.

The standard for competency to be _____ or executed is virtually identical to that for competency to stand trial: Whether the convicted individual _____ the nature of the proceedings and an ability to _____ in the process.

sentenced

understands
participate

The rationale for requiring that the convicted individual be competent for the sentencing and punishment phases is similar to the rationale for requiring that the defendant be competent to stand trial: to preserve the integrity of the sentencing and punishment process; to ensure that the convicted individual will have the ability to contest the decision through all stages of appeal prior to imposition of punishment; and to ensure that the deterrent function of punishment is served by punishing only those who have the requisite mental capacity to be sentenced or punished.

The rationale for requiring that the convicted individual be _____ for the sentencing and punishment phases is similar to the rationale for requiring that the defendant be competent to stand _____: to preserve the integrity of the sentencing and _____ process; to ensure that the convicted individual will have the ability to contest the decision through all stages of appeal prior to imposition of punishment; and to ensure that the deterrent function of punishment is served by punishing only those who have the requisite mental capacity to be sentenced or punished.

competent

trial
punishment

The American Psychiatric Association's position on ethical issues in death penalty cases is set forth in a 1990 Ethics Committee Opinion that stated: "It is unethical for a psychiatrist to participate in executions. It is not unethical for a psychiatrist to conduct a competency evaluation in which the prisoner is told of the interview's purpose and the limitations on confidentiality."

The American Psychiatric Association's position on ethical issues in death penalty cases is set forth in a 1990 Ethics Committee Opinion that stated: "It is _____ for a psychiatrist to participate in executions. It is not unethical for a psychiatrist to conduct a _____ evaluation in which the prisoner is told of the interview's purpose and the limitations on confidentiality."

unethical

competency

In addition to ethical quandaries, capital punishment raises several questions of constitutional law that have special relevance for psychiatrists who might be asked to evaluate competency to be executed. In *Estelle v. Smith* (U.S. 1982), the Court held that Smith's Fifth Amendment rights to be free from self-incrimination and Sixth Amendment right to assistance of counsel were denied when the state's psychiatrist, who had examined him solely for assessing competency to stand trial, was allowed to testify as to Smith's dangerousness at the penalty phase and Smith was not informed of the purpose of the evaluation or right to the presence of counsel.

In addition to ethical quandaries, capital punishment raises several questions of _____ *law that have special relevance for psychiatrists who might be asked to evaluate competency to be executed. In* Estelle v. Smith *(U.S. 1982), the Court held that Smith's Fifth Amendment rights to be free from self-incrimination and Sixth Amendment right to assistance of counsel were denied when the state's psychiatrist, who had examined him solely for assessing competency to stand trial, was allowed to testify as to Smith's dangerousness at the penalty phase and Smith was not informed of the* _____ *of the evaluation or right to the presence of counsel.*

constitutional

purpose

In *Barefoot v. Estelle* (U.S. 1983), the Court held that although the state could not compel a defendant to undergo a psychiatric evaluation, there is no constitutional barrier to allowing psychiatric experts to testify to the defendant's future dangerousness at the penalty phase based on hypothetical questions.

In Barefoot v. Estelle *(U.S. 1983), the Court held that although the state could not compel a defendant to undergo a* _____ *evaluation, there is no constitutional barrier to allowing psychiatric experts to testify to the defendant's future* _____ *at the penalty phase based on hypothetical questions.*

psychiatric

dangerousness

The American Psychiatric Association (APA) filed an *amicus curiae* (friend of the court) brief in the case, pointing out the unreliability of dangerousness predictions. The Court rejected the arguments in that brief, holding that such assessments are not so inherently unreliable that they should be excluded totally and that the lack of reliability can be addressed as a credibility issue on cross examination.

The American Psychiatric Association (APA) filed an amicus curiae *(friend of the* _____*) brief in the case, pointing out the unreliability of* _____ *predictions. The Court rejected the arguments in that brief, holding that such assessments are not so inherently unreliable that they should be excluded totally and that the lack of reliability can be addressed as a credibility issue on cross examination.*

court
dangerousness

The Supreme Court has held that imposition of the death penalty on an individual with mild or moderately severe intellectual disability is not unconstitutional *per se*. However, a Texas statute that did not allow the jury to consider mitigating factors such as a history of intellectual disability (formerly called mental retardation) and child abuse but did allow consideration of aggravating factors was unconstitutional (*Penry v. Lynaugh* [U.S. 1989]).

The Supreme Court has held that imposition of the death penalty on an individual with mild or moderately severe intellectual disability is not unconstitutional per se. However, a Texas statute that did not allow the jury to consider mitigating factors such as a history of _____ _____ (formerly called mental retardation) and child abuse but did allow consideration of aggravating factors was unconstitutional (Penry v. Lynaugh [U.S. 1989]).

intellectual; disability

Forced administration of antipsychotic medication to rendering the inmate competent to be executed raises important questions of constitutional law. Some states consider this permissible, whereas others hold that doing so violates constitutional principles such as the right to privacy and constitutes cruel, excessive, and unusual punishment (*Louisiana v. Perry* [La. 1992]).

Forced administration of _____ medication to rendering the inmate _____ to be executed raises important questions of constitutional law. Some states consider this permissible, while others hold that doing so violates _____ principles such as the right to privacy, and constitutes cruel, excessive, and unusual punishment (Louisiana v. Perry [La. 1992]).

antipsychotic
competent

constitutional

The Eighth Amendment prohibition against execution of incompetent mentally ill prisoners as cruel and unusual punishment was extended to other categories of defendants convicted on capital charges. These include those with moderately severe intellectual disability (*Atkins v. Virginia* [U.S., 2002]) and those who committed their offenses when they were younger than 18 years of age (*Roper v. Simmons* [U.S., 2005]).

The Eighth Amendment prohibition against execution of _____ mentally ill prisoners as cruel and unusual _____ was extended to other catego- ries of defendants convicted on capital charges. These include those with moderately severe intellectual dis- ability (Atkins v. Virginia [U.S., 2002]) and those who committed their offenses when they were younger than 18 years of age (Roper v. Simmons [U.S., 2005]).

incompetent
punishment

Criminal Responsibility

For an act to be criminal, there must be both a guilty act (the *actus reus*) and guilty intent (*mens rea*). *Mens rea*, in the narrow sense, is the mental state required as an element of a specific crime; for example, larceny is knowingly taking possession of property that is not yours, for your own use, and with the intent of depriv- ing the true owner of its use. In the general sense, *mens rea* refers to blameworthiness or legal liability.

For an act to be _____, there must be both a guilty _____ (the actus reus*) and guilty _____ (*mens rea*)*. Mens rea, *in the narrow sense, is the _____ state required as an ele- ment of a specific crime; for example, larceny is know- ingly taking possession of property that is not yours, for your own use, and with the intent of depriving the true owner of its use. In the general sense,* mens rea *refers to blameworthiness or _____ liability.*

criminal
act
intent
mental

legal

The defense of lack of criminal responsibility/not guilty by reason of insanity is based on the concept that some individuals who commit criminal acts should not be held morally blameworthy because they cannot be considered moral agents due to their men- tal state (Moore, 1984).

The defense of lack of criminal responsibility/not guilty by reason of _____ *is based on the concept that some individuals who commit* _____ *acts should not be held* _____ *blameworthy because they cannot be considered moral agents due to their mental state (Moore, 1984).*

insanity
criminal
morally

Voluntary intoxication is not a basis for an insanity defense, although it can provide a basis for a diminished capacity defense. Mental illness caused by substance abuse, exacerbation of an existing mental illness due to intoxication, and pathologic intoxication can all provide a basis for an insanity defense.

_____ *intoxication is not a basis for an insanity defense, although it can provide a basis for a diminished* _____ *defense. Mental illness caused by substance abuse, exacerbation of an existing mental illness due to intoxication, and pathologic intoxication can all provide a basis for an* _____ *defense.*

Voluntary

capacity

insanity

Evolution of the Insanity Defense Standards

Legal standards for the insanity defense have evolved over the years, but they have continued to utilize the same core elements. One of the best-known standards is the *M'Naghten test* (England, 1843): "To establish a defense on the ground of insanity, it must be clearly proved that, at the time of the committing of the act the party accused was laboring under such a defect of reason, from disease of the mind, as not to *know* the nature and quality of the act he was doing, or, if he did *know* it, that he did not *know* he was doing what was wrong."

Legal standards for the insanity defense have evolved over the years, but they have continued to utilize the same core elements. One of the best-known standards is the _____ _____ (England, 1843): "To establish a defense on the ground of _____, it must be clearly proved that, at the time of the committing of the act the party accused was laboring under such a defect of reason, from disease of the mind, as not to know *the nature and quality of the act he was doing, or, if he did* know *it, that he did not* know *he was doing what was _____."*

M'Naghten; test
insanity

wrong

The M'Naghten test is a cognitive test, focusing only on whether the defendant knew what he was doing or that what he was doing was wrong.

The M'Naghten test is a _____ test, focusing only on whether the defendant _____ what he was doing or that what he was doing was _____.

cognitive
knew

wrong

On the theory that individuals with mental illness or intellectual disability (formerly called mental retardation) might be able to appreciate that a certain behavior is wrong but not be able to control themselves, the English courts established the *Irresistible Impulse/ Loss of Control Test* in *Rex v. Davis* (England, 1881).

On the theory that individuals with mental illness or intellectual _____ (formerly called mental retardation) might be able to appreciate that a certain behavior is _____ but not be able to _____ themselves, the English courts established the Irresistible _____*/Loss of Control* Test *in Rex v. Davis (England, 1881).*

disability

wrong
control
Impulse

The Irresistible Impulse/Loss of Control Test was adopted and appended to the M'Naghten test in the United States in the case of *Alabama v. Parson* (Alabama, 1887).

The Irresistible Impulse/Loss of Control Test was adopted and appended to the M'Naghten test in the United States in the case of Alabama v. _____ *(Alabama, 1887).*

Parson

Under this rule, a defendant with a mental disease or defect would be held not responsible for criminal acts, even if he could tell right from wrong, if such disease or defect deprived him of power to choose right from wrong, *and* the alleged crime was so connected with the mental disease as to have been the product of it solely. As such, this is a volitional rather than a cognitive test.

Under this rule, a defendant with a mental disease or defect would be held not _____ for criminal acts, even if he could tell right from _____, if such disease or defect deprived him of power to _____ right from wrong, and *the alleged crime was so connected with the mental disease as to have been the product of it solely. As such, this is a _____ rather than a cognitive test.*

responsible
wrong
choose

volitional

The combination of the M'Naghten rule and the Irresistible Impulse/Loss of Control Test provided the basis for the *Model Penal Code/American Law Institute* (ALI) standard that is still used in many states: "A person is not responsible for criminal conduct if at the time of such conduct as a result of mental disease or defect he lacks substantial capacity either to appreciate the criminality (wrongfulness) of his conduct or to conform his conduct to the requirements of the law."

The combination of the M'Naghten rule and the Irresistible Impulse/Loss of _____ Test provided the basis for the Model Penal Code/American Law Institute *(ALI) standard that is still used in many states: "A person is not _____ for criminal conduct if at the time of such conduct as a result of mental disease or defect he lacks substantial _____ either to appreciate the criminality (wrongfulness) of his conduct or to conform his conduct to the requirements of the law."*

Control

responsible

capacity

For the purposes of that standard, the terms "mental disease or mental defect" do not include an abnormality manifested only by repeated criminal or otherwise antisocial behavior.

For the purposes of that standard, the terms "mental disease or mental defect" do not include an abnormality manifested only by repeated criminal or otherwise _____ behavior.

antisocial

This standard requires the presence of a mental disease or defect, but excludes personality or other disorders that have antisocial behaviors as their primary symptoms; for example, pedophilia, pyromania, and antisocial personality disorder itself.

This standard requires the presence of a _____ disease or defect, but excludes personality or other disorders that have _____ behaviors as their primary symptoms; for example, pedophilia, pyromania, and antisocial personality disorder itself.

mental

antisocial

The disorder must cause an impairment in functioning that has a clear and direct causal connection or relationship with the alleged criminal act.

The disorder must cause an impairment in _____ *that has a clear and direct causal connection or relationship with the alleged criminal act.*

functioning

John Hinckley's assassination attempt on President Reagan, and his subsequent insanity acquittal, gave rise to calls for modification and narrowing of the federal insanity defense standard. With the guidance of the APA, Congress adopted the following standard for federal criminal cases: "It is an affirmative defense to a prosecution under any Federal statute that, at the time of the commission of the acts constituting the offense, the defendant, as a result of a severe mental disease or defect, was unable to appreciate the nature and quality or the wrongfulness of his acts."

John Hinckley's assassination attempt on President Reagan, and his subsequent insanity acquittal, gave rise to calls for modification and narrowing of the federal insanity _____ *standard. With the guidance of the APA, Congress adopted the following standard for federal criminal cases: "It is an affirmative defense to a prosecution under any Federal statute that, at the time of the commission of the acts constituting the offense, the defendant, as a result of a severe* _____ *disease or defect, was unable to* _____ *the nature and quality or the wrongfulness of his acts."*

defense

mental
appreciate

Unlike the ALI/Model Penal Code standard, the new federal standard requires an *inability* to appreciate the nature and quality or wrongfulness, not merely a lack of substantial capacity. The underlying mental disease or defect must be severe, and the lack of knowledge or appreciation complete—lacking substantial capacity so not sufficient.

Unlike the ALI/Model Penal Code standard, the new federal standard requires an _____ to appreciate the nature and quality or _____, not merely a lack of substantial capacity. The underlying mental disease or defect must be severe, and the lack of knowledge or _____ complete—lacking substantial capacity so not sufficient.

inability
wrongfulness

appreciation

When a defendant is found not guilty by reason of insanity, he or she is generally remanded to a specialized facility, often a forensic hospital, where the person's level of dangerousness and need for security are assessed.

When a defendant is found not _____ by reason of insanity, he or she is generally remanded to a _____ facility, often a forensic hospital, where the person's level of _____ and need for security are assessed.

guilty

specialized
dangerousness

In rare cases, the acquitted defendant might be released directly to the community, but it is far more common for the person to be committed to the hospital for at least some period, especially if the crime was one of violence.

In rare cases, the _____ defendant might be released directly to the community, but it is far more common for the person to be _____ to the hospital for at least some period, especially if the crime was one of violence.

acquitted

committed

Guilty but mentally ill (GBMI) is a criminal defense that was developed as an alternative to the insanity defense, but it can be offered by a state as an additional option for the trier of fact (judge or jury).

Guilty but mentally ill *(GBMI) is a* _____ *criminal*
defense that was developed as an alternative to the
insanity defense, but it can be offered by a state as an
additional option for the trier of fact (judge or jury).

An individual found GBMI is not legally insane and
is held responsible for the act but is acknowledged to
have been mentally ill at the time of the act. It is available in a limited number of states.

An individual found GBMI is not _____ *legally*
insane and is held responsible for the act but is
acknowledged to have been mentally ill at the time of
the _____ *. It is available in a limited number* *act*
of states.

Diminished capacity is a defense that can be raised
whereby an individual suffers from a mental illness or
cognitive deficit but does not meet the requirements
of the insanity defense, but nevertheless provides a
basis for not holding the person fully responsible for
the behavior. The result is usually to reduce the level
of the conviction; for example, reduction of the finding of guilt from first-degree murder to second-degree
murder.

Diminished _____ *is a defense that can be* *capacity*
raised whereby an individual suffers from a men-
tal illness or cognitive deficit but does not meet the
requirements of the _____ *defense, but never-* *insanity*
theless provides a basis for not holding the person fully
_____ *for the behavior. The result is usually to* *responsible*
reduce the _____ *of the conviction; for exam-* *level*
ple, reduction of the finding of guilt from first-degree
murder to second-degree murder.

Demographics of the Insanity Defense

Contrary to public perception, the insanity defense is not widely used, generally successful, or a "rich man's defense." It is raised in 0.1% of felony trials, and there are two insanity pleas per 1,000 felony arrests. The success rate for the insanity defense varies by state.

Contrary to public perception, the insanity defense is not widely used, generally successful, or a "rich man's defense." It is raised in _____*% of felony trials, and there are* _____ *insanity pleas per 1,000 felony arrests. The success rate for the insanity defense varies by state.*

0.1
two

Overall, juries hand down only 5% of insanity acquittals, 40% to 50% are decided by judges, and the rest are the result of plea bargains. Insanity acquittees tend to be young (20 to 30 years old), white, with on average an eighth-grade education, and unskilled workers.

Overall, juries hand down only _____*% of insanity acquittals, 40% to 50% are decided by judges, and the rest are the result of plea bargains. Insanity* _____ *tend to be young (20 to 30 years old), white, with on average an eighth-grade education, and unskilled workers.*

5

acquittees

The Role of Psychiatrists in the Legal System

The first encounter psychiatrists have with the legal system commonly occurs when a patient becomes involved in litigation and the psychiatrist receives a subpoena for medical records or is asked to testify at a deposition or trial.

The first encounter _____ *have with the legal* psychiatrists
system commonly occurs when a patient becomes
involved in litigation and the psychiatrist receives
a _____ *for medical records or is asked to* subpoena
_____ *at a deposition or trial.* testify

Whether the psychiatrist submits the records or testifies is governed by the legal concept of psychotherapist–patient privilege.

Whether the psychiatrist submits the records or tes-
tifies is governed by the legal concept of psychothera-
pist–patient _____. privilege

The psychotherapist–patient privilege is a corollary of confidentiality. Psychiatrists have an ongoing duty of confidentiality; that is, to protect the privacy of information revealed by patients during treatment.

The psychotherapist–patient _____ *is a corol-* privilege
lary of confidentiality. Psychiatrists have an ongoing
duty of _____; *that is, to protect the privacy* confidentiality
of information revealed by _____ *during* patients
treatment.

Testimonial privilege is the right to have matters revealed to a physician or therapist held in confidence and not revealed in an administrative or judicial proceeding, without the patient's permission, except under certain circumstances.

Testimonial _____ *is the right to have mat-* privilege
ters revealed to a physician or therapist held in confi-
dence and not revealed in an administrative or judicial
_____, *without the patient's permission,* proceeding
except under certain circumstances.

Whereas confidentiality is an ongoing obligation on the part of the physician, the privilege belongs to, and can be raised or waived only by the patient: if the patient does not raise the privilege, the physician can be compelled to testify.

Whereas confidentiality is an ongoing obligation on the part of the _____, the privilege belongs to, and can be raised or waived only by the _____: if the patient does not raise the privilege, the physician can be compelled to testify.

physician
patient

Testimonial privilege in its modern form can be claimed regarding communications with psychotherapists, physicians, clergy members, spouses, and attorneys.

Testimonial _____ in its modern form can be claimed regarding communications with psychotherapists, physicians, clergy members, spouses, and attorneys.

privilege

Privileges were not an original part of the English common law, which held that the "King is entitled to everyman's evidence." However, it was eventually decided that society gained more from protecting the special relationships covered by the privileges and that it was more important than the information that would be excluded by application of the privilege.

Privileges were not an original part of the English _____ law, which held that the "King is entitled to everyman's evidence." However, it was eventually decided that society gained more from protecting the special relationships covered by the _____ and that it was more important than the information that would be excluded by application of the privilege.

common

privileges

The psychotherapist–patient privilege exists in all 50 states, the District of Columbia, and all federal courts (*Jaffee v. Redmond* [U.S. 1996]).

The psychotherapist–_____ privilege exists in all 50 states, the District of Columbia, and all federal courts (Jaffee v. Redmond [U.S. 1996]).

patient

Just as there are exceptions to confidentiality, there are exceptions to the testimonial privilege. These exceptions include the following: express waiver by the patient (the patient expressly waives his or her right to exercise the privilege by putting his or her mental status at issue in the course of litigation; e.g., claiming emotional damages in a personal injury suit); mandated reporting (e.g., cases of child abuse); and statutory exceptions (e.g., when the patient is involved in billing disputes or malpractice litigation against the physician).

Just as there are exceptions to confidentiality, there are exceptions to the testimonial _____. These exceptions include the following: express _____ by the patient (the patient expressly waives his or her right to exercise the privilege by putting his or her mental status at issue in the course of litigation; e.g., claiming emotional damages in a personal injury suit); mandated reporting (e.g., cases of child abuse); and, statutory _____ (e.g., when the patient is involved in billing disputes or malpractice litigation against the physician).

privilege
waiver

exceptions

The Psychiatrist As Forensic Evaluator/Expert Witness

Broadly defined, a forensic evaluation is any psychiatric evaluation concerning issues that relate to litigation or administrative proceedings or might do so. No clinical care is provided in a forensic evaluation, and it does not create a doctor–patient relationship in the traditional sense.

Broadly defined, a _____ evaluation is any psychiatric evaluation concerning issues that relate to litigation or administrative proceedings or might do so. No clinical care is provided in a _____ evaluation, and it does not create a doctor–patient relationship in the traditional sense.

forensic

forensic

Whereas a treating clinician has a fiduciary obligation to act only in the best interests of the patient, the forensic evaluator's primary obligation is to the party requesting the evaluation. The client in a forensic evaluation might be the attorney, court, or agency that has retained the psychiatrist.

Whereas a treating clinician has a _____ obligation to act only in the best interests of the patient, the forensic evaluator's primary _____ is to the party _____ the evaluation. The _____ in a forensic evaluation might be the attorney, court, or agency that has retained the psychiatrist.

fiduciary

obligation

requesting; client

Despite that, forensic evaluators have an obligation to be objective, honest, and to take appropriate actions if the patient is found to pose a threat of harm to himself or herself or others.

Despite that, _____ evaluators have an obligation to be objective, honest, and to take appropriate actions if the patient is found to pose a threat of
_____ to himself or herself or others.

forensic

harm

Confidentiality is absent in a forensic evaluation
because, by definition, it is being conducted on behalf
of a third party who has requested it.

Confidentiality is absent in a _____ evaluation because, by definition, it is being conducted on
behalf of a _____ party who has requested it.

forensic

third

As a result, the forensic evaluator has an ethical obligation and, in some states, a legal obligation to obtain
informed consent from the evaluee before conducting
the examination. This includes warning the evaluee
about the limitations on confidentiality.

As a result, the forensic evaluator has an ethical obligation and, in some states, a legal _____ to
obtain informed consent from the _____ before
conducting the examination. This includes warning
the evaluee about the limitations on _____.

obligation

evaluee

confidentiality

The Psychiatrist As Expert Witness

An expert witness is a witness who has knowledge
related to the subject matter of the litigation beyond
that of the average juror or judge, and who can offer
information that will be useful to the judge or jury in
reaching a decision in the matter.

An expert witness is a witness who has _____
related to the subject matter of the litigation beyond
that of the _____ juror or judge, and who can
offer information that will be useful to the judge or jury
in reaching a decision in the matter.

knowledge

average

Anyone with such additional knowledge can technically be accepted as an expert, although the credibility of the expert might be attacked. For example, a medical student might be accepted as an expert in medicine based on his or her studies, but the credibility of that expert would be attacked based on the lack of experience.

Anyone with such additional knowledge can technically be accepted as an _____, *although the* _____ *of the expert might be attacked. For example, a medical student might be accepted as an expert in medicine based on his or her studies, but the* _____ *of that expert would be attacked based on the lack of experience.*

expert
credibility

credibility

Psychiatric experts may use any information they would normally use during an evaluation as a basis for testimony, including hearsay (information that they did not obtain firsthand, but rather obtained through the reports of a third party).

Psychiatric _____ *may use any information they would normally use during an evaluation as a basis for* _____, *including hearsay (information that they did not obtain firsthand, but rather obtained through the reports of a third party).*

experts

testimony

However, some states require that if the expert is to use hearsay evidence from another person, the source of that information must be available for cross examination.

However, some states require that if the expert is to use hearsay evidence from another person, the source of that information must be available for cross _____.

examination

The job of the expert witness is to provide scientifically and clinically accurate testimony in an ethically responsible manner and to provide answers to the legal questions raised in the proceeding, to the extent possible.

The job of the _____ witness is to provide scientifically and clinically accurate _____ in an ethically responsible manner and to provide answers to the legal questions raised in the proceeding, to the extent possible.

expert
testimony

When a psychiatrist is designated as an expert witness, he or she can provide the court with an expert opinion on an issue before the court; for example, whether the care of a patient was below the standard of care (malpractice) or whether the defendant has a mental illness that rendered him unable to conform his behavior to the requirements of the law (criminal responsibility). Not all jurisdictions require that the judge formally declare the psychiatrist to be an expert. However, all jurisdictions give judges authority to exclude expert testimony if it is unnecessary to assist the trier of fact, is unduly prejudicial, or does not have solid scientific grounding.

When a psychiatrist is designated as an expert witness, he or she can provide the court with an expert opinion on an issue before the court; for example, whether the care of a patient was below the standard of care (_____) or whether whether the defendant has a mental illness that rendered him unable to conform his behavior to the requirements of the law (criminal _____). Not all jurisdictions require that the judge formally declare the psychiatrist to be an expert. However, all jurisdictions give judges authority to exclude expert testimony if it is unnecessary to assist the trier of fact, is unduly prejudicial, or does not have solid scientific grounding.

malpractice

responsibility

The fact witness is not allowed to offer such opinions.

The _____ witness is not allowed to offer such opinions.

The Psychiatrist As Fact Witness

A fact witness is an individual who has firsthand information related to the matter being decided. There are no special requirements to be a fact witness, other than firsthand knowledge relevant to the case. Anyone, including a child, can be a fact witness.

A fact witness is an individual who has firsthand _____ related to the matter being decided. There are no special requirements to be a fact witness, other than _____ hand knowledge relevant to the case. Anyone, including a child, can be a fact _____.

A fact witness cannot offer an expert opinion or use hearsay.

A fact witness cannot offer an _____ opinion or use _____.

A treating psychiatrist might be called to testify about the mental condition of a patient in a wide variety of settings; for example, personal injury litigation, worker's compensation claims, administrative hearings, and even criminal cases.

A _____ psychiatrist might be called to testify about the mental condition of a patient in a wide variety of settings; for example, personal injury litigation, worker's compensation claims, administrative hearings, and even criminal cases.

The rules of the psychotherapist–patient privilege apply if the patient raises it; however, the psychiatrist must testify if the patient does not raise the privilege. Even if the privilege is raised, the Court might decide that it does not apply and order the psychiatrist to testify.

The rules of the psychotherapist–patient _____   privilege
apply if the patient raises it; however, the psychiatrist
must _____ *if the patient does not raise the*   testify
privilege. Even if the privilege is raised, the Court
might decide that it does not apply and order the psy-
chiatrist to testify.

Refusal to testify can lead to a finding of contempt of court, justifying a fine or jail time.

Refusal to _____ *can lead to a finding of con-*   testify
tempt of court, justifying a fine or jail time.

When a patient is involved in litigation but does not put his mental status in issue by claiming emotional distress damages, the records of the treating psychiatrist generally cannot be obtained. However, if the patient claims emotional damages, the records and testimony of the treating physician can be obtained by the other side.

When a patient is involved in litigation but does not
put his _____ *status in issue by claiming emo-*   mental
tional distress damages, the records of the treating
psychiatrist generally cannot be obtained. However,
if the patient _____ *emotional damages, the*   claims
records and testimony of the treating physician can be
obtained by the other side.

Malpractice and Boundary Violations

Overview

- Claims of medical malpractice can arise from unintentional errors during medical treatment or from intentional acts.
- Boundary violations are behaviors on the part of the physician that violate standards for appropriate relationships between doctors and patients. Sexual relationships with patients are the most notorious of these.

Theoretical Basis

- Medical malpractice is a subset of personal injury law. It exists to provide compensation for those injured by the negligent acts of others.
- Boundary violations are a departure from the standard of care and, as such, can be the basis for a malpractice claim. Although they are considered departures from the standard of care, they are intentional torts, and most malpractice insurers have adopted provisions that might provide for defense of the allegations but not pay the damages if the psychiatrist is found liable.

Clinical Applications

- To prove a claim of malpractice, the plaintiff claiming to have been injured must establish that the defendant physician was derelict in fulfilling a duty of care owed to the patient, resulting in direct and foreseeable damage to the plaintiff.
- There are recognized standards for the relationships between doctors and patients. Some of these standards are more flexible under some circumstances. For example, psychiatrists generally should not have business relationships with patients. However, in small communities, certain business relationships might be acceptable because of limited options.
- On the other end of the spectrum, sexual relations with patients is always deemed to be unethical, is the basis for license revocation, is considered a criminal offense in some states, and can be the basis for malpractice suit.

Malpractice Law

Malpractice cases are part of the general field of personal injury or tort law.

Malpractice cases are part of the general field of personal _____ or _____ law.

injury; tort

Torts are defined as civil wrongs in which one person injures another, giving rise to a right to sue for damages. In comparison, crimes are offenses against society, as represented by the government.

Torts are defined as _____ wrongs in which one person injures another, giving rise to a right to sue for _____. In comparison, _____ are offenses against society, as represented by the government.

civil

damages; crimes

The penalties for a crime can be monetary, confinement or other restriction on freedom (like probation), or in some cases and jurisdictions, death—that is, capital punishment.

The _____ for a crime can be monetary, confinement or other restriction on freedom (like probation), or in some cases and jurisdictions, death—that is, capital punishment.

penalties

There are two types of torts: intentional and unintentional.

There are two types of torts: intentional and _____.

unintentional

Intentional torts are those in which the purpose of the action is the harmful act itself; for example, sexual contact with a patient or physical assault on a patient (both of which involve purposeful physical contact with the victim).

_____ torts are those in which the purpose of the action is the harmful act itself; for example, sexual contact with a patient or physical assault on a patient (both of which involve purposeful physical contact with the victim).

Intentional

Unintentional torts arise when some harm occurs because a person has not exercised adequate care (referred to as negligence), such as when a patient is injured during treatment, allegedly because the defendant practitioner did not exercise appropriate care; in other words, medical negligence.

_____ torts arise when some harm occurs because a person has not exercised adequate care (referred to as _____), such as when a patient is injured during treatment, allegedly because the defendant practitioner did not exercise appropriate care; in other words, medical negligence.

Unintentional

negligence

Malpractice insurance is intended to cover acts of negligence (i.e., unintentional torts); however, it will also cover intentional torts that are a component of legitimate treatment, such as a complaint of assault and battery arising from physical restraint of an agitated patient.

Malpractice insurance is intended to cover acts of _____ (i.e., unintentional _____); however, it will also cover intentional torts that are a component of legitimate treatment, such as a complaint of assault and battery arising from physical restraint of an agitated patient.

negligence; torts

Where there is no clinical justification for the intentional act, such as in sexual misconduct, malpractice insurers might cover the cost of defending the case, but not any damages awarded if liability is found.

Where there is no clinical justification for the intentional act, such as in _____ misconduct, malpractice insurers might cover the cost of defending the case, but not any _____ awarded if liability is found.

sexual

damages

To prove a malpractice claim, a plaintiff (the party who claims to have been injured and who is seeking damages) must establish the four elements (the "four Ds") of a malpractice claim.

To prove a _____ claim, a plaintiff (the party who claims to have been injured and who is seeking damages) must establish the four elements (the "four Ds") of a malpractice claim.

malpractice

Dereliction of duty. The defendant was derelict in his or her responsibilities. This can be established either by showing that the treating clinician departed from or ignored the standard of care, or by establishing that the treating clinician followed the standard of care but did so in an inept fashion.

Dereliction of _____. *The defendant was derelict in his or her responsibilities. This can be established either by showing that the treating clinician departed from or ignored the _____ of care, or by establishing that the treating clinician followed the standard of care but did so in an _____ fashion.*

duty

standard

inept

Duty. In the Anglo-American legal system, there is no specific duty of care to another person unless the two parties have a "special relationship," such as between doctor and patient. The defendant had a specific obligation or duty to the patient to act with reasonable care. The general duty of physicians is to possess and employ such reasonable skill and care as are commonly had and are exercised by respectable, average physicians in the same or similar community.

Duty. *In the Anglo-American legal system, there is no specific duty of care to another person unless the two parties have a "special relationship," such as between doctor and patient. The defendant had a specific obligation or duty to the patient to act with reasonable care. The general* _____ *of physicians is to* — duty
possess and employ such reasonable skill and care as are commonly had and are exercised by respectable, _____ *physicians in the same or similar* — average
community.

Specialists are held to a higher standard of performance because they hold themselves out to the community as having special expertise. A physician who holds him or herself out as an expert in a specific area will be judged according to this higher standard, regardless of the actual credentials.

_____ *are held to a higher standard of perfor-* — Specialists
mance because they hold themselves out to the community as having special expertise. A physician who holds him or herself out as an _____ *in a spe-* — expert
cific area will be judged according to this higher standard, regardless of the actual credentials.

The *School Rule*: Practice in accordance with the standards of a recognized school of thought or training will be judged according to the standards of that school to which the defendant physician is a member. For example, cognitive-behavioral therapists should be judged according to the standard of care for that school of treatment, not according to a psychoanalytic standard of care.

The School Rule: *Practice in accordance with the standards of a recognized school of thought or training will be judged according to the _____ of that school to which the defendant physician is a member. For example, cognitive-behavioral therapists should be judged according to the standard of care for that school of treatment, not according to a psychoanalytic standard of care.*

standards

However, all clinicians who hold themselves out to the public as being qualified to diagnose and treat illnesses are held to the same basic standard of care regarding safety, assessment, and conduct. For example, a psychiatrist cannot excuse himself or herself from failing to diagnose his patent's myocardial infarction on the basis that he does not prescribe medication and only does psychotherapy.

However, all clinicians who hold themselves out to the public as being qualified to diagnose and treat illnesses are held to the same basic _____ of care regarding safety, assessment, and conduct. For example, a psychiatrist _____ excuse himself or herself from failing to diagnose his patent's myocardial infarction on the basis that he does not prescribe medication and only does psychotherapy.

standard

cannot

In addition to the duty to possess and employ reasonable care, physicians have a duty to consult; that is, to seek out consultation when the limits of the physician's knowledge and experience have been exceeded.

In addition to the duty to possess and employ reasonable _____, physicians have a duty to _____; that is, to seek out consultation when the limits of the physician's knowledge and experience have been exceeded.

care

consult

Direct causation of damages. Direct causation has two separate components. (1) A mechanical notion assessed by the *But for rule*: "But for" the negligent behavior, the injury would not have occurred. (2) Proximate or legal causation: the harm that occurred was a "reasonably foreseeable" consequence of the negligent action.

_____ *causation of* _____. Direct causation has two separate components. *(1) A mechanical notion assessed by the* But for rule: *"_____ for" the _____ behavior, the injury would not have occurred. (2) Proximate or legal causation: the harm that occurred was a "reasonably _____"* consequence of the negligent action.

In proving causation, a plaintiff might invoke the evidentiary concept of *res ipsa loquitur* (the thing speaks for itself) when the cause of injury to the plaintiff was under the sole control of the defendant and the defendant alone has knowledge of the injurious event.

In proving _____, a plaintiff might invoke the evidentiary concept of res ipsa loquitur *(the _____ speaks for itself) when the cause of injury to the plaintiff was under the sole control of the defendant and the defendant alone has knowledge of the injurious event.*

In such cases, the presumption is that the defendant was responsible for the injury, and the defendant must rebut that presumption.

In such cases, the presumption is that the defendant was _____ for the injury, and the defendant must rebut that presumption.

Damages must be proven. Unless damages can be proven, the malpractice suit will not succeed, even if there was negligent performance of a duty. Damages can be of three types: economic damages (such as lost earnings, the cost of medical treatment for the injury, or the cost of paying for someone to perform household services the victim can no longer perform because of the injury); physical damages (such as loss of a bodily function); and emotional pain and suffering.

Damages must be proven. Unless _____ can be proven, the _____ suit will not succeed, even if there was negligent performance of a duty. Damages can be of three types: _____ damages (such as lost earnings, the cost of medical treatment for the injury, or the cost of paying for someone to perform household services the victim can no longer perform because of the injury); _____ damages (such as loss of a bodily function); and _____ pain and suffering.

damages
malpractice

economic

physical
emotional

Selected Malpractice Issues

Abandonment can be either intentional (e.g., the doctor decides he or she no longer wants to see a patient), or unintentional (e.g., while planning to do so, the doctor forgets to arrange for cover during vacation).

Abandonment can be either intentional (e.g., the doctor decides he or she no longer wants to see a patient), or _____ (e.g., while planning to do so, the doctor forgets to arrange for cover during vacation).

unintentional

Abandonment is defined as the unilateral termination of the doctor–patient relationship, by the doctor, without consent or justification, in which the termination results in harm to the patient.

_____ *is defined as the unilateral termination of the doctor–patient relationship, by the doctor, without consent or _____, in which the termination results in harm to the patient.*

Abandonment

justification

After there is a doctor–patient relationship, the physician has a duty to continue to provide care until one or the other party ends it.

After there is a doctor–patient relationship, the physician has a _____ to continue to provide care until one or the other party ends it.

duty

Physicians always have the right to end the treatment relationship; however, there is an obligation to give the patient an opportunity to find alternative care, to cooperate in the transition to a new caregiver, and to make the patient aware of options for emergency coverage.

Physicians always have the right to end the treatment relationship; however, there is an obligation to give the patient an opportunity to find _____ care, to cooperate in the transition to a new caregiver, and to make the patient aware of options for emergency _____.

alternative

coverage

Ideally, from both the clinical and medical–legal perspectives, this transition takes place over time as part of a proper termination. There are situations, however, in which the physician is justified in unilaterally terminating the relationship, in some cases abruptly, and providing more limited support in the transition.

Ideally, from both the clinical and medical–legal perspectives, this transition takes place over time as part of a proper termination. There are situations, however, in which the physician is justified in unilaterally _____ the relationship, in some cases abruptly, and providing more limited support in the transition.

terminating

These situations include: no-show patients who repeatedly fail to keep their appointments; assaultive or abusive patients; and non-compliant patients.

These situations include: no-show patients who repeatedly fail to keep their _____; assaultive or _____ patients; and non-_____ patients.

appointments
abusive; compliant

When it is necessary to terminate the relationship, claims of abandonment can be avoided by providing a referral to another clinician or agency, access to emergency coverage, and medications between the time of termination and the time of the appointment with the new treater.

When it is necessary to _____ the relationship, claims of _____ can be avoided by providing a _____ to another clinician or agency, access to emergency _____, and medications between the time of termination and the time of the appointment with the new treater.

terminate
abandonment
referral
coverage

Abandonment allegations can arise when the physician is away for vacation or conferences and fails to provide coverage or provides sub-standard coverage. The physician can avoid these allegations by providing adequate coverage during absences. The physician is responsible for insuring that the coverage is competent and available.

_____ allegations can arise when the physician is away for vacation or conferences and fails to provide coverage or provides sub-standard coverage. The physician can avoid these allegations by providing adequate _____ during absences. The physician is responsible for insuring that the coverage is competent and _____.

Abandonment

coverage

available

For example, a physician can be held liable if harm occurs to a patient during his or her absence and he or she knows or should have known that the covering physician was incompetent.

For example, a physician can be held _____ if harm occurs to a patient during his or her absence and he or she knows or should have known that the covering physician was _____.

liable

incompetent

Vicarious Liability

Vicarious liability is the imposition of liability on one party for the negligent acts of another.

Vicarious _____ is the imposition of liability on one party for the negligent acts of another.

liability

Under the doctrine of *respondeat superior* (let the master answer), the "master" (employer) can be held liable for the negligent acts of a second person, the "servant" (employee), committed within the scope of the employment. A master, for these purposes, is one who has direct authority over the servant, as evidenced by the power to hire or fire and veto power over the servant's decisions.

Under the doctrine of respondeat _____ *(let the master answer), the "master" (_____) can be held liable for the negligent acts of a second person, the "servant" (_____), committed within the scope of the employment. A master, for these purposes, is one who has direct _____ over the servant, as evidenced by the power to hire or fire and veto power over the servant's decisions.*

Superior
employer

employee

authority

A consultant is distinguished from a master or employer by being outside the direct line of responsibility for the acts of the second person, having no direct authority over the second person, and offering advice and direction on a "take it or leave it" basis.

A _____ is distinguished from a master or employer by being outside the direct line of _____ for the acts of the second person, having no direct authority over the second person, and offering advice and direction on a "take it or leave it" basis.

consultant

responsibility

This concept applies to the supervision of residents as well as to the supervision of non-physicians.

This concept applies to the supervision of _____ as well as to the supervision of non-physicians.

residents

In addition, at times physicians might be asked by non-physician colleagues to write prescriptions or to sign disability forms for patients whom they have not evaluated. By signing the form as the attending of record, the physician can be held to the same level of responsibility for any harm that occurs, just as if he or she had personally evaluated the patient.

In addition, at times physicians might be asked by non-physician colleagues to write prescriptions or to sign disability forms for patients whom they have not evaluated. By signing the form as the attending of record, the physician can be held to the same level of _____ for any harm that occurs, just as if he or she had personally _____ the patient.

responsibility
evaluated

Confidentiality

Confidentiality is the physician's duty to keep information revealed by the patient during treatment private and not disclose it to unauthorized parties.

_____ *is the physician's duty to keep informa-*   Confidentiality
tion revealed by the patient during treatment private
and not disclose it to unauthorized parties.

The *Health Insurance Portability and Accountability Act* (HIPAA) is a federal statute that imposes, among other things, requirements for maintaining the confidentiality of patient information, referred to as Protected Health Information (PHI).

The Health Insurance Portability and Accountability   federal
Act *(HIPAA) is a* _____ *statute that imposes,*
among other things, requirements for maintaining the   confidentiality
_____ *of patient information, referred to as*   Health
Protected _____ *Information (PHI).*

Those HIPAA requirements are preempted by state confidentiality laws that provide a higher level of protection. There are multiple exceptions (e.g., emergencies, waiver of confidentiality, incapacity) to the general duty of confidentiality, both in state laws and in HIPAA.

Those _____ *requirements are preempted*   HIPAA
by _____ *confidentiality laws that provide a*   state
_____ *level of protection. There are multiple*   higher
exceptions (e.g., emergencies, waiver of confidentiality,
incapacity) to the general duty of confidentiality, both
in state laws and in HIPAA.

An *emergency* is defined as a situation in which failure to breach confidentiality would result in a serious outcome; for example, life-threatening deterioration in the patient's condition, or imminent risk to self or others.

An emergency *is defined as a situation in which*
_____ *to breach confidentiality would result*   failure
in a serious outcome; for example, life-threatening
deterioration in the patient's condition, or imminent
risk to self or others.

Another exception is a *waiver of confidentiality* by the patient or other appropriate decision maker.

Another exception is a waiver of _____ *by the patient or other appropriate decision maker.*

confidentiality

Incapacity occurs when the patient is temporarily or permanently unable to make decisions, in which case information can be released about the patient in order to provide care. However, when a substitute decision maker is identified, that individual can insist that the patient's confidentiality be protected.

Incapacity occurs when the patient is temporarily or permanently _____ *to make decisions, in which case information can be released about the patient in order to provide care. However, when a* _____ *decision maker is identified, that individual can insist that the patient's confidentiality be protected.*

unable

substitute

Various state and federal laws provide exceptions to confidentiality, such as releases of information required during civil commitment proceedings, malpractice cases, bill collections, and litigation in which the patient puts his or her mental status at issue.

Various state and federal laws provide _____ *to confidentiality, such as releases of information required during civil commitment proceedings, malpractice cases, bill collections, and litigation in which the patient puts his or her* _____ *status at issue.*

exceptions

mental

Breaches of confidentiality might be required by statute or case law, such as obligations to report child abuse or neglect, or the duty to take steps to protect third parties from harm threatened by a patient.

Breaches of confidentiality might be _____ by statute or case law, such as obligations to report child _____ or neglect, or the duty to take steps to protect third parties from harm threatened by a _____.

required

abuse

patient

In the normal course of treatment, information about a patient can be shared with a limited group of individuals without getting the express permission of the patient. These are generally held to include the patient, co-treaters, consultants, supervisors, and facilities to which the patient is being admitted or transferred.

In the normal course of treatment, information about a patient can be shared with a limited group of individuals without getting the express _____ of the patient. These are generally held to include the patient, co-treaters, consultants, supervisors, and facilities to which the patient is being _____ or transferred.

permission

admitted

Before information is released to family members, referring clinicians, lawyers, or law enforcement, the patient's expressed permission should be obtained.

Before information is _____ to family members, referring clinicians, lawyers, or law enforcement, the patient's expressed _____ should be obtained.

released

permission

In all cases for which confidentiality is to be breached, it should be breached to the least extent possible and with a reasonable effort to inform the patient.

In all cases for which _____ is to be breached, it should be breached to the _____ extent possible and with a reasonable effort made to inform the patient.

confidentiality
least

The Duty to Protect Third Parties: The *Tarasoff* Legacy

Breach of confidentiality is ethically permissible when it is necessary to protect the patient or third parties: "Psychiatrists at times may find it necessary in order to protect the patient or the community from imminent danger, to reveal confidential information disclosed by the patient" (*Principles of Medical Ethics with Annotations Especially Applicable to Psychiatry*, Sec.4, Annotation 8).

Breach of _____ is ethically permissible when it is necessary to protect the patient or _____ parties: "Psychiatrists at times may find it necessary in order to protect the patient or the community from imminent danger, to reveal confidential information disclosed by the patient" (Principles of Medical Ethics with Annotations Especially Applicable to Psychiatry, Sec.4, Annotation 8).

confidentiality
third

The legal obligation to act to protect third parties from one's patient is generally framed as follows: there is a basic duty to protect or warn if a therapist knows or should know of a patient's potential for substantial harm to an identified or readily identifiable individual.

The legal obligation to act to _____ third parties from one's patient is generally framed as follows: there is a basic duty to protect or warn if a therapist knows or should know of a patient's potential for substantial _____ to an identified or readily identifiable individual.

protect

harm

The key case in this area is *Tarasoff v. Regents of the University of California*, 551 P. 2d 334 (1976), in which the court held that: "When a therapist determines, or pursuant to the standards of his profession should determine, that his patient presents a serious danger of violence to another, he incurs a serious obligation to use reasonable care to protect the intended victim from such danger."

The key case in this area is _____ *v. Regents of the University of California, 551 P. 2d 334 (1976), in which the court held that: "When a therapist determines, or pursuant to the standards of his profession should determine, that his patient presents a serious danger of violence to another, he incurs a serious obligation to use reasonable care to protect the intended* _____ *from such danger."*

Tarasoff

victim

Implications of the *Tarasoff* Decision

Psychotherapists and patients have a special relationship that sets the stage for the therapist being held uniquely liable for some actions of the patient. The duty that was established by *Tarasoff* was to an identified victim, although subsequent cases expanded the duty to broader classes of individuals and, in some cases, to unidentified individuals who might reasonably be foreseen to be possible victims.

Psychotherapists and patients have a special relationship that sets the stage for the therapist being held uniquely _____ *for some actions of the patient. The duty that was established by* _____ *was to an identified victim, although subsequent cases expanded the duty to broader classes of individuals and, in some cases, to unidentified individuals who might reasonably be foreseen to be possible victims.*

liable
Tarasoff

The "Tarasoff Duty" is not necessarily a duty to warn the intended victim or law enforcement, which would require a breach of confidentiality, but a duty to protect that can be fulfilled through a variety of other actions on the part of the treater.

The "_____ Duty" is not necessarily a duty to warn the intended victim or law enforcement, which would require a breach of confidentiality, but a duty to _____ that can be fulfilled through a variety of other actions on the part of the treater.

Tarasoff

protect

The duty to protect third parties has been rejected or modified by courts and legislatures in multiple states, in response to the rapid expansion of the duty in many jurisdictions.

The duty to protect _____ parties has been rejected or modified by courts and legislatures in multiple states, in response to the rapid expansion of the duty in many jurisdictions.

third

The APA developed a model statute that provides for liability to third parties for the acts of a patient where there is:

> "Communication of an explicit threat to identified victim(s) with apparent intent and ability to carry out the threat, and reasonable steps are not taken; or the patient has a known history of physical violence, and the therapist has a "reasonable basis to believe that there is a clear and present danger that the patient will attempt to kill or inflict serious bodily injury against a reasonably identified victim or victims"; and reasonable steps are not taken."

The APA developed a model statute that provides for _____ to third parties for the acts of a patient where there is:

> "Communication of an explicit threat to identified victim(s) with apparent intent and ability to carry out the threat, and reasonable steps are not taken; or the patient has a known history of physical violence, and the therapist has a "reasonable basis to believe that there is a clear and present danger that the patient will attempt to kill or inflict serious bodily injury against a reasonably identified victim or victims"; and reasonable steps are not taken."

Reasonable steps are defined in the model statute as one or more of the following: warning a potential victim or victims; notifying law enforcement in the area; arranging for voluntary hospitalization; or taking appropriate steps to involuntarily hospitalize the patient.

Reasonable steps are defined in the model statute as one or more of the following: _____ a potential victim or victims; notifying _____ enforcement in the area; arranging for voluntary _____; or taking appropriate steps to involuntarily hospitalize the patient.

liability

warning
law
hospitalization

The National Practitioner Data Bank

The National Practitioner Data Bank (NPDB) was authorized by the *Health Care Quality Improvement Act* of 1986 (HCQIA). The database applies to physicians, dentists, and, as of 2010, all other health care practitioners.

The National Practitioner Data Bank (NPDB) was authorized by the Health Care _____ *Improvement Act of 1986 (HCQIA). The database applies to physicians, dentists, and, as of 2010, all other health care practitioners.*

Quality

The HCQIA requires health care organizations to report the following to the central Data Bank: payments made to satisfy malpractice claims (including settlements); adverse privilege actions taken by health care entities; and actions taken on licensure. The practitioner who is reported to the NPDB must be notified and given an opportunity to respond.

The HCQIA requires health care _____ *to report the following to the central Data Bank: payments made to satisfy* _____ *claims (including settlements); adverse privilege actions taken by health care entities; and actions taken on* _____. *The practitioner who is reported to the NPDB must be notified and given an opportunity to respond.*

organizations

malpractice

licensure

In 2010, Section 1921 of the *Social Security Act* expanded the range of information to be collected by the NPDB to include negative actions or findings by state licensing agencies, peer-review organizations, and private accreditation organizations against all health care practitioners and organizations.

In 2010, Section 1921 of the Social _____ *Act expanded the range of information to be collected by the NPDB to include negative actions or findings by state licensing agencies, peer-review organizations, and private accreditation organizations against all health care practitioners and organizations.*

Security

Hospitals, including human resource departments and nurse recruitment departments, nursing homes, other health care organizations, as well as Quality Improvement Organizations can register and obtain access to all NPDB data.

Hospitals, including human resource departments and nurse recruitment departments, nursing homes, other health care organizations, as well as Quality _____ Organizations can register and obtain access to all NPDB data.

Improvement

Boundary Violations

An Introduction to Professional Boundaries

Boundaries between doctors and patients provide a set of rules and expectations that allow the patient to develop trust in the physician and to know what to expect from the relationship.

_____ between doctors and patients provide a set of rules and expectations that allow the patient to develop _____ in the physician and to know what to expect from the relationship.

Boundaries

trust

Boundary crossings involve minor but potentially important blurring of the boundaries. *Boundary violations* involve more clear-cut transgressions of the accepted boundaries between doctor and patient.

Boundary _____ involve minor but potentially important blurring of the boundaries. Boundary _____ involve more clear-cut transgressions of the accepted boundaries between doctor and patient.

crossings

violations

What constitutes a boundary crossing or violation is determined both by the nature of the action and the setting in which it occurs. For example, in a rural area it might be appropriate for the family doctor to spend time with patients at a social gathering, whereas the same socializing for a doctor in an urban practice might be considered a boundary crossing.

What constitutes a boundary crossing or violation is determined both by the _____ of the action nature
and the _____ in which it occurs. For example, setting
in a rural area it might be appropriate for the family doctor to spend time with patients at a social gathering, whereas the same socializing for a doctor in an _____ practice might be considered a bound- urban
ary crossing.

The maintenance of professional boundaries has been the subject of both ethical and legal proscriptions, not to mention a source of malpractice lawsuits. The core principle underlying these constraints on physician behavior is that physicians have a fiduciary duty to their patients; that is, an obligation to put the patient's interests above his or her own.

The maintenance of professional boundaries has been the subject of both ethical and legal proscriptions, not to mention a source of malpractice lawsuits. The core principle underlying these constraints on physician behavior is that physicians have a _____ fiduciary
duty to their patients; that is, an obligation to put the patient's interests above his or her own.

The Hippocratic Oath includes admonitions about maintaining appropriate boundaries, including maintaining confidences and avoiding sexual relations. In 1989, the American Medical Association Council on Ethical and Judicial Affairs passed an ethical rule that prohibits physician–patient sexual contact, regardless of specialty.

The _____ Oath includes admonitions about maintaining appropriate boundaries, including maintaining confidences and avoiding sexual relations. In 1989, the American Medical Association Council on Ethical and Judicial Affairs passed an ethical rule that prohibits physician–patient _____ contact, regardless of _____.

Hippocratic

sexual
specialty

Physician–patient sexual contacts, and other forms of physician exploitation of patients, are the basis for discipline by physician registration authorities in all states. The APA has adopted an ethical guideline that declares it unethical for a psychiatrist to have a sexual relationship with a former or current patient.

Physician–patient sexual contacts, and other forms of physician exploitation of patients, are the basis for _____ by physician registration authorities in _____ states. The APA has adopted an ethical guideline that declares it unethical for a psychiatrist to have a sexual relationship with a _____ or current patient.

discipline
all

former

Several states have enacted laws that make it a *criminal offense* for a physician to have a sexual relationship with a patient. States that have criminalized this behavior vary as to whether they classify doctor-patient sexual contact as a misdemeanor or felony. Some statutes distinguish between first and repeated offenses.

Several states have enacted laws that make it a _____ offense for a physician to have a _____ relationship with a patient. States that have criminalized this behavior vary as to whether they classify doctor–patient sexual contact as a misdemeanor or _____. Some statutes distinguish between first and repeated offenses.

criminal
sexual

felony

Although many of the statutes criminalize psychotherapist–patient sexual contact, the term "psychotherapy" is broadly defined in some statutes as "the professional treatment, assessment, or counseling of a mental or emotional illness, symptom, or condition." Thus, many of these statutes would apply to primary-care physicians who treat psychiatric conditions. Statutes also differ regarding how they define "patient" and whether and when the prohibition applies.

Although many of the statutes criminalize _____– psychotherapist–
patient sexual contact, the term psychotherapy is
broadly defined in some statutes as "the professional
treatment, assessment, or counseling of a mental
or emotional illness, symptom, or condition." Thus,
many of these statutes would apply to _____- primary-
_____ physicians who treat psychiatric condi- care
tions. Statutes also differ regarding how they define
"patient" and whether and when the prohibition
applies.

Selected Boundary Issues

Business Dealings Between Doctor and Patient

The physician–patient relationship is fundamentally a business relationship. The terms of the contract are that the physician receives a fee in return for helping the patient with medical problems.

The physician—patient relationship is fundamentally
a _____ relationship. The terms of the con- business
tract are that the physician receives a fee in return for
helping the patient with medical problems.

The arms-length nature of the relationship allows the physician to be objective in his or her dealings with the patient. Involvement in other business dealings can detract from the distance, objectivity, and empathy necessary for the physician–patient relationship to succeed and is prohibited except under special circumstances; for example, the psychiatrist lives in a small community where the patient operates the only hardware store. Even in this limited situation, the psychiatrist would be well advised to find another store in a neighboring town.

The arms-length nature of the relationship allows the physician to be _____ in his or her dealings with the patient. Involvement in other _____ dealings can detract from the distance, objectivity, and empathy necessary for the physician–patient relationship to succeed and is prohibited except under special circumstances; for example, the psychiatrist lives in a small community where the patient operates the only hardware store. Even in this limited situation, the psychiatrist would be well advised to find another store in a neighboring town.

objective
business

Social (Non-Sexual) Relationships with Patients

In certain settings (e.g., small towns), social contact between psychiatrist and patient is unavoidable. Confidentiality and cordiality without undue familiarity can allow these treatment relationships to succeed.

In certain settings (e.g., small towns), social contact between psychiatrist and patient is unavoidable. _____ and cordiality without undue familiarity can allow these treatment relationships to succeed.

Confidentiality

Confidentiality

Close friendships between physician and patient can compromise the physician's objectivity and lead to errors in judgment because of the physician's emotional involvement. The same principles apply here as apply in the context of physicians treating family members.

Close friendships between physician and patient can _____ the physician's objectivity and lead to errors in _____ because of the physician's emotional involvement. The same principles apply here as apply in the context of physicians treating _____ members.

compromise
judgment

family

Sex in the Treatment Relationship

As indicated earlier, sexual relations with patients has been the subject of great legal and ethical attention. The reasons why physicians become involved in these relationships vary. They include predatory sexual behavior by physicians seeking to take advantage of the patient, but more commonly, infatuation on the part of physicians who are vulnerable to engaging in such violations because of their own life circumstances and psychological issues.

As indicated earlier, sexual relations with patients has been the subject of great legal and ethical attention. The reasons why physicians become involved in these relationships vary. They include _____ sexual behavior by physicians seeking to take advantage of the patient, but more commonly, _____ on the part of physicians who are vulnerable to engaging in such violations because of their own life circumstances and psychological issues.

predatory

infatuation

Some patients can be seductive, or at least engage in behavior that might be interpreted by the physician as seductive. Nevertheless, it is always the physician's responsibility to maintain appropriate boundaries.

Some patients can be _____, or at least engage in behavior that might be interpreted by the physician as seductive. Nevertheless, it is always the physician's _____ to maintain appropriate boundaries.

seductive

responsibility

Failure to do so is always the fault of the physician. Sex with patients in the guise of treatment constitutes fraud and misrepresentation and can provide the basis for criminal prosecution in some states.

Failure to do so is always the fault of the _____ Sex with patients in the guise of treatment constitutes fraud and misrepresentation and can provide the basis for _____ prosecution in some states.

physician

criminal

Sexual relationships with patients in many cases result from the disparity in power and authority between doctor and patient. Such relationships are inherently coercive and without consent and are clear examples of the violation of the physician's fiduciary duty to the patient.

Sexual relationships with patients in many cases result from the disparity in _____ and authority between doctor and patient. Such relationships are inherently coercive and without _____ and are clear examples of the violation of the physician's _____ duty to the patient.

power

consent

fiduciary

Patients who have had sexual relationships with their physicians often suffer significant harm as a result. Such injury becomes a justifiable basis for a lawsuit against the physician.

Patients who have had _____ relationships   sexual
with their physicians often suffer significant harm as
a result. Such injury becomes a justifiable basis for a
_____ against the physician.   lawsuit

Even though involvement in a sexual relationship with
a patient constitutes an intentional tort that would
ordinarily not be covered by malpractice insurance,
courts have held that it represents a mishandling of
the transference and countertransference in the treatment relationship, thus putting it within the realm of
malpractice.

Even though involvement in a sexual relationship with
a patient constitutes an _____ tort that would   intentional
ordinarily not be covered by malpractice insurance,
courts have held that it represents a mishandling of
the _____ and countertransference in the   transference
treatment relationship, thus putting it within the realm
of malpractice.

Post-Reading Quiz

Post-Reading Quiz: Answer Sheet

1. _____
2. _____
3. _____
4. _____
5. _____
6. _____
7. _____
8. _____
9. _____
10. _____
11. _____
12. _____
13. _____
14. _____
15. _____
16. _____
17. _____
18. _____
19. _____
20. _____

21. _____

22. _____

23. _____

24. _____

25. _____

26. _____

27. _____

28. _____

29. _____

30. _____

31. _____

32. _____

33. _____

34. _____

35. _____

36. _____

37. _____

38. _____

39. _____

40. _____

41. _____

42. _____

43. _____

44. _____

45. _____

46. _____

47. _____

48. _____

49. _____

50. _____

Post-Reading Quiz: Questions

1. Which of the following is at the core of the Anglo-American legal system?
   A. Case law
   B. Civil law
   C. Criminal law
   D. Malpractice law

2. Which type of law is predominantly based on statutes enacted by legislatures?
   A. Case law
   B. Civil law
   C. Criminal law
   D. Malpractice law

3. Which of the following types of law is a subset of tort law?
   A. Civil law
   B. Criminal law
   C. Malpractice law
   D. Tax law

4. Which of the following, if absent, can lead to a victim suing for damages stemming from unpermitted touching?
   A. Consent
   B. Payment
   C. Pleasure
   D. Witnesses

5. Which of the following is the term used when a failure to act would likely lead to an imminent, serious, and negative effect on a patient's condition?

    A. An emergency
    B. A futile situation
    C. As soon as possible (ASAP)
    D. An urgent situation

6. Which of the following terms is described by "consent given after a sharing of knowledge and a chance to consider alternative options"?

    A. Capacity
    B. Informed consent
    C. Simple consent
    D. The professional standard

7. Which of the following (in addition to having the appropriate information and competency) is a legal requirement for informed consent?

    A. Absence of an emergency
    B. Absence of psychosis
    C. The ability to speak
    D. Voluntariness

8. When a clinician provides the amount of information that an average patient would require to make a decision under the same circumstances, it is said to meet which of the following conditions?

    A. Competency
    B. Simple consent
    C. The materiality standard
    D. The professional standard

9. For a patient to give informed consent, he or she must have which of the following?

A. A desire to improve

B. A high school education

C. Less than 6 out of 10 on the pain scale

D. The capacity to make informed decisions

10. True or False. The capacity to accept a procedure is the same as it is to refuse a procedure.

A. True

B. False

11. Which of the following terms used by courts strips a person of certain rights and privileges normally accorded to adults?

A. Delirium

B. Dementia

C. Incompetence

D. Schizophrenia

12. After a psychiatrist determines that a patient lacks the capacity to refuse a non-emergent procedure, the treating team should do which of the following?

A. Administer an antipsychotic agent to enhance cooperation

B. Seek out an alternative decision-maker

C. Treat the patient as he or she would any patient with that condition

D. Withhold the treatment refused by the patient

13. Which of the following terms denotes the capacity to serve as a witness in court?

A. Global capacity

B. Professional capacity

C. Testamentary capacity

D. Testimonial capacity

14. Which of the following pairs of authors created the standard approach to the assessment of decision-making capacity?
    A. Appelbaum and Grisso
    B. Hackett and Cassem
    C. Kahana and Bibring
    D. Stanton and Schwartz

15. Which of the following is a key component of the capacity assessment?
    A. Determining whether the patient agrees with the recommendations of the provider
    B. Determining whether the patient can pay for the services recommended
    C. Determining whether the patient has had a similar procedure before
    D. Determining whether the patient has a factual understanding of the information provided

16. True or False. A person can be deemed competent to make their own treatment decisions but still be unable to manage their financial affairs.
    A. True
    B. False

17. Which of the following is an exception to obtaining fully informed consent?
    A. An acute psychotic illness
    B. A disagreement with the treating physician
    C. An emergency
    D. A terminal illness

18. True or False. All competent people have a right to make their own medical treatment decisions, even when the individual is suffering from a serious mental illness or is civilly committed.
    A. True
    B. False

19. True or False. The standard of proof is lower for civil commitment cases than it is for ordinary civil cases and for criminal cases.
    A. True
    B. False

20. Which of the following is the standard of proof needed for criminal cases?
    A. A lack of remorse for the crime
    B. Beyond a reasonable doubt
    C. Clear and convincing evidence
    D. Eye-witness testimony

21. Criteria for civil commitment can include which of the following?
    1. Dangerousness to self as evidenced by threats or attempts to cause self-harm
    2. Dangerousness to others as evidenced by threats or attempts to cause harm
    3. Dangerousness to self as evidenced by inability to provide for oneself
    4. Inability to make informed decisions regarding treatment of one's mental illness
        A. 1 & 2
        B. 2 & 4
        C. 1, 2, & 3
        D. All of the above

22. Exceptions to informed consent include which of the following?
    1. Emergency
    2. Incompetence
    3. Waiver
    4. Patient would be dissuaded from making the right decision
        A. 1 & 2
        B. 2 & 4
        C. 1, 2, & 3
        D. All of the above

23. Which of the following is the standard of proof to be considered competent to stand trial?

    A. Ability to understand the charges against one

    B. Beyond a reasonable doubt

    C. Preponderance of the evidence

    D. Scoring ≥ 26 on the Mini-Mental State Examination

24. Which of the following is the focus of competency evaluations to stand trial?

    A. The defendant's mental state at the time of the alleged act

    B. The defendant's mental state at the time of the proceedings

    C. The defendant's educational history

    D. The defendant's history of a psychotic illness

25. True or False. The defendant's consent is not necessary for a competency evaluation; the court can order it over the defendant's objection.

    A. True

    B. False

26. True or False. The Eighth Amendment prohibits execution of incompetent mentally ill prisoners as cruel and unusual punishment.

    A. True

    B. False

27. True or False. For an act to be criminal, there must be both a guilty act (the *actus reus*) and guilty intent (*mens rea*); that is, the mental state required as an element of a specific crime.

    A. True

    B. False

28. True or False. Mental illness caused by substance abuse, exacerbation of an existing mental illness due to intoxication, and pathologic intoxication does not provide a basis for an insanity defense.

    A. True

    B. False

29. Which of the following has served as the basis for the legal standards of the insanity defense?

    A. Atkins test

    B. M'Naghten test

    C. Penry test

    D. Roper test

30. Which of the following is a cognitive test, focusing only on whether the defendant knew what he was doing or that what he was doing was wrong?

    A. Atkins test

    B. M'Naghten test

    C. Penry test

    D. Roper test

31. Which of the following is the usual disposition when a defendant is found not guilty by reason of insanity?

    A. A correctional facility

    B. A freestanding psychiatric hospital

    C. A general hospital

    D. Their home

32. Which of the following is a defense that can be raised where an individual suffers from a mental illness or cognitive deficit that does not meet the requirements of the insanity defense, but nevertheless provides a basis for not holding the person fully responsible for the behavior?

    A. Antisocial personality

    B. Diminished capacity

    C. Incompetence

    D. Voluntary intoxication

33. In what percentage of cases is the insanity defense raised in felony trials?
    A. 0.1%
    B. 1%
    C. 5%
    D. 10%

34. True or False. Juries hand down 5% of insanity acquittals, whereas 40% to 50% are decided by judges; the remainder are a result of plea bargains.
    A. True
    B. False

35. In which of the following situations do psychiatrists who work within general hospitals typically first become involved with the legal system?
    A. When a psychiatrist receives a subpoena for medical records
    B. When a psychiatrist is asked to determine whether an individual is competent to stand trial
    C. When a psychiatrist is asked to determine if an individual has the capacity to make a will
    D. When a psychiatrist is asked to determine if an individual qualifies for an insanity defense

36. True or False: The forensic evaluator's primary obligation is to the individual being evaluated.
    A. True
    B. False

37. True or False. There is no doctor-patient relationship in a forensic evaluation.
    A. True
    B. False

38. True or False. Confidentiality is limited in a forensic evaluation because it is being conducted on behalf of a third party who has requested the evaluation.

    A. True
    B. False

39. Which of the following is the term used to describe a witness who has knowledge related to the subject matter of the litigation beyond that of the average juror or judge, and who can offer information that will be useful to the judge or jury in reaching a decision in the matter?

    A. Credible witness
    B. Expert witness
    C. Fact witness
    D. Officer of the court

40. Which of the following terms is used to describe an individual who has firsthand knowledge related to the matter being decided?

    A. Credible witness
    B. Expert witness
    C. Fact witness
    D. Officer of the court

41. The reasons for requiring that the defendant be competent to stand trial during criminal proceedings include:

    1. It makes the trial go faster.
    2. It preserves the integrity of the legal system.
    3. It makes the defense attorney's job easier.
    4. It helps to ensure a fair trial.

        A. 1 & 3
        B. 2 & 4
        C. 1, 2, & 3
        D. All of the above

42. True statements about the psychotherapist–patient privilege include:
    1. Unlike confidentiality, the patient must raise the privilege to keep the physician from testifying.
    2. A treating clinician might be required to testify concerning otherwise-confidential information about his or her patient if the patient asks the clinician to do so (express waiver).
    3. A treating clinician might be required to testify concerning otherwise-confidential information about his or her patient if the patient has put his mental state in issue as part of the legal proceedings (implied waiver).
    4. The treating clinician believes it is in the patient's best interests.
       A. 1 & 2
       B. 2 & 4
       C. 1, 2, & 3
       D. All of the above

43. Which of the following are elements of a malpractice claim?
    1. Departure from the standard of care
    2. Existence of a duty of care
    3. Direct or proximate causation
    4. Damages
       A. 1 & 3
       B. 2 & 4
       C. 1, 2, & 3
       D. All of the above

44. Sexual relations with a patient can result in which of the following?
    1. Suspension or loss of the psychiatrist's medical license
    2. Ethical censure
    3. A malpractice claim
    4. Criminal conviction
       A. 1 & 3
       B. 2 & 4
       C. 1, 2, & 3
       D. All of the above

45. True or False. Dereliction of duty can be established either by showing that the treating clinician departed from (or ignored) the standard of care or by establishing that the treating clinician followed the standard of care but did so in an inept fashion.

    A. True

    B. False

46. True or False. The general duty of physicians is to possess and employ such reasonable skill and care as are commonly had and are exercised by respectable, average physicians in the same or similar community.

    A. True

    B. False

47. True or False. A physician who holds him or herself out as an expert in a specific area will be judged according to this higher standard, regardless of the actual credentials.

    A. True

    B. False

48. True or False. In a malpractice case, the plaintiff does not need to prove that there are damages; it is sufficient to show that there was a negligent performance of a duty.

    A. True

    B. False

49. True or False. Abandonment, in malpractice cases, can be either intentional (e.g., the doctor decides that he or she no longer wants to see a patient), or unintentional (e.g., while planning to do so, the doctor forgets to arrange for cover during vacation).

    A. True

    B. False

50. True or False. Abandonment is defined as the unilateral termination of the doctor-patient relationship, by the patient, without consent or justification, in which the termination results in harm to the patient.

    A. True

    B. False

Post-Reading Quiz: Answer Key

Note: This answer key should be viewed after taking the pre-test, reading the text, and taking the post-reading quiz.

1. _____A_____
2. _____C_____
3. _____A_____
4. _____A_____
5. _____A_____
6. _____B_____
7. _____D_____
8. _____C_____
9. _____D_____
10. _____B_____
11. _____C_____
12. _____B_____
13. _____D_____
14. _____A_____
15. _____D_____
16. _____A_____
17. _____C_____
18. _____A_____
19. _____A_____
20. _____B_____

*Answers continued on next page.

21. _____C_____

22. _____C_____

23. _____C_____

24. _____B_____

25. _____A_____

26. _____A_____

27. _____A_____

28. _____B_____

29. _____B_____

30. _____B_____

31. _____B_____

32. _____B_____

33. _____A_____

34. _____A_____

35. _____A_____

36. _____B_____

37. _____A_____

38. _____A_____

39. _____B_____

40. _____C_____

41. _____B_____

42. _____C_____

43. _____D_____

44. _____D_____

45. _____A_____

46. _____A_____

47. _____A_____

48. _____B_____

49. _____A_____

50. _____B_____

PRE-TEST SCORE:
_____ (Number of correct answers)
_____ (Percent of correct answers)

POST-READING SCORE:
_____ (Number of correct answers)
_____ (Percent of correct answers)

Post-Reading Quiz: Answers

1. Which of the following is at the core of the Anglo-American legal system?
   A. **Case law**
   B. Civil law
   C. Criminal law
   D. Malpractice law

2. Which type of law is predominantly based on statutes enacted by legislatures?
   A. Case law
   B. Civil law
   C. **Criminal law**
   D. Malpractice law

3. Which of the following types of law is a subset of tort law?
   A. **Civil law**
   B. Criminal law
   C. Malpractice law
   D. Tax law

4. Which of the following, if absent, can lead to a victim suing for damages stemming from unpermitted touching?
   A. **Consent**
   B. Payment
   C. Pleasure
   D. Witnesses

5. Which of the following is the term used when a failure to act would likely lead to an imminent, serious, and negative effect on a patient's condition?

    A. **An emergency**

    B. A futile situation

    C. As soon as possible (ASAP)

    D. An urgent situation

6. Which of the following terms is described by "consent given after a sharing of knowledge and a chance to consider alternative options"?

    A. Capacity

    B. **Informed consent**

    C. Simple consent

    D. The professional standard

7. Which of the following (in addition to having the appropriate information and competency) is a legal requirement for informed consent?

    A. Absence of an emergency

    B. Absence of psychosis

    C. The ability to speak

    D. **Voluntariness**

8. When a clinician provides the amount of information that an average patient would require to make a decision under the same circumstances, it is said to meet which of the following conditions?

    A. Competency

    B. Simple consent

    C. **The materiality standard**

    D. The professional standard

9. For a patient to give informed consent, he or she must have which of the following?

   A. A desire to improve

   B. A high school education

   C. Less than 6 out of 10 on the pain scale

   D. **The capacity to make informed decisions**

10. True or False. The capacity to accept a procedure is the same as it is to refuse a procedure.

   A. True

   B. **False**

11. Which of the following terms used by courts strips a person of certain rights and privileges normally accorded to adults?

   A. Delirium

   B. Dementia

   C. **Incompetence**

   D. Schizophrenia

12. After a psychiatrist determines that a patient lacks the capacity to refuse a non-emergent procedure, the treating team should do which of the following?

   A. Administer an antipsychotic agent to enhance cooperation

   B. **Seek out an alternative decision-maker**

   C. Treat the patient as he or she would any patient with that condition

   D. Withhold the treatment refused by the patient

13. Which of the following terms denotes the capacity to serve as a witness in court?

   A. Global capacity

   B. Professional capacity

   C. Testamentary capacity

   D. **Testimonial capacity**

14. Which of the following pairs of authors created the standard approach to the assessment of decision-making capacity?
    A. **Appelbaum and Grisso**
    B. Hackett and Cassem
    C. Kahana and Bibring
    D. Stanton and Schwartz

15. Which of the following is a key component of the capacity assessment?
    A. Determining whether the patient agrees with the recommendations of the provider
    B. Determining whether the patient can pay for the services recommended
    C. Determining whether the patient has had a similar procedure before
    D. **Determining whether the patient has a factual understanding of the information provided**

16. True or False. A person can be deemed competent to make their own treatment decisions but still be unable to manage their financial affairs.
    A. **True**
    B. False

17. Which of the following is an exception to obtaining fully informed consent?
    A. An acute psychotic illness
    B. A disagreement with the treating physician
    C. **An emergency**
    D. A terminal illness

18. True or False. All competent people have a right to make their own medical treatment decisions, even when the individual is suffering from a serious mental illness or is civilly committed.
    A. **True**
    B. False

19. True or False. The standard of proof is lower for civil commitment cases than it is for ordinary civil cases and for criminal cases.

A. **True**

B. False

20. Which of the following is the standard of proof needed for criminal cases?

A. A lack of remorse for the crime

B. **Beyond a reasonable doubt**

C. Clear and convincing evidence

D. Eye-witness testimony

21. Criteria for civil commitment can include which of the following?

1. Dangerousness to self as evidenced by threats or attempts to cause self-harm

2. Dangerousness to others as evidenced by threats or attempts to cause harm

3. Dangerousness to self as evidenced by inability to provide for oneself

4. Inability to make informed decisions regarding treatment of one's mental illness

A. 1 & 2

B. 2 & 4

C. **1, 2, & 3**

D. All of the above

22. Exceptions to informed consent include which of the following?

1. Emergency

2. Incompetence

3. Waiver

4. Patient would be dissuaded from making the right decision

A. 1 & 2

B. 2 & 4

C. **1, 2, & 3**

D. All of the above

23. Which of the following is the standard of proof to be considered competent to stand trial?

A. Ability to understand the charges against one

B. Beyond a reasonable doubt

C. **Preponderance of the evidence**

D. Scoring ≥ 26 on the Mini-Mental State Examination

24. Which of the following is the focus of competency evaluations to stand trial?

A. The defendant's mental state at the time of the alleged act

B. **The defendant's mental state at the time of the proceedings**

C. The defendant's educational history

D. The defendant's history of a psychotic illness

25. True or False. The defendant's consent is not necessary for a competency evaluation; the court can order it over the defendant's objection.

A. **True**

B. False

26. True or False. The Eighth Amendment prohibits execution of incompetent mentally ill prisoners as cruel and unusual punishment.

A. **True**

B. False

27. True or False. For an act to be criminal, there must be both a guilty act (the *actus reus*) and guilty intent (*mens rea*); that is, the mental state required as an element of a specific crime.

A. **True**

B. False

28. True or False. Mental illness caused by substance abuse, exacerbation of an existing mental illness due to intoxication, and pathologic intoxication does not provide a basis for an insanity defense.

A. True

B. **False**

29. Which of the following has served as the basis for the legal standards of the insanity defense?

   A. Atkins test

   B. **M'Naghten test**

   C. Penry test

   D. Roper test

30. Which of the following is a cognitive test, focusing only on whether the defendant knew what he was doing or that what he was doing was wrong?

   A. Atkins test

   B. **M'Naghten test**

   C. Penry test

   D. Roper test

31. Which of the following is the usual disposition when a defendant is found not guilty by reason of insanity?

   A. A correctional facility

   B. **A freestanding psychiatric hospital**

   C. A general hospital

   D. Their home

32. Which of the following is a defense that can be raised where an individual suffers from a mental illness or cognitive deficit that does not meet the requirements of the insanity defense, but nevertheless provides a basis for not holding the person fully responsible for the behavior?

   A. Antisocial personality

   B. **Diminished capacity**

   C. Incompetence

   D. Voluntary intoxication

33. In what percentage of cases is the insanity defense raised in felony trials?
    A. **0.1%**
    B. 1%
    C. 5%
    D. 10%

34. True or False. Juries hand down 5% of insanity acquittals, whereas 40% to 50% are decided by judges; the remainder are a result of plea bargains.
    A. **True**
    B. False

35. In which of the following situations do psychiatrists who work within general hospitals typically first become involved with the legal system?
    A. **When a psychiatrist receives a subpoena for medical records**
    B. When a psychiatrist is asked to determine whether an individual is competent to stand trial
    C. When a psychiatrist is asked to determine if an individual has the capacity to make a will
    D. When a psychiatrist is asked to determine if an individual qualifies for an insanity defense

36. True or False: The forensic evaluator's primary obligation is to the individual being evaluated.
    A. True
    B. **False**

37. True or False. There is no doctor-patient relationship in a forensic evaluation.
    A. **True**
    B. False

38. True or False. Confidentiality is limited in a forensic evaluation because it is being conducted on behalf of a third party who has requested the evaluation.

    A. **True**
    B. False

39. Which of the following is the term used to describe a witness who has knowledge related to the subject matter of the litigation beyond that of the average juror or judge, and who can offer information that will be useful to the judge or jury in reaching a decision in the matter?

    A. Credible witness
    B. **Expert witness**
    C. Fact witness
    D. Officer of the court

40. Which of the following terms is used to describe an individual who has firsthand knowledge related to the matter being decided?

    A. Credible witness
    B. Expert witness
    C. **Fact witness**
    D. Officer of the court

41. The reasons for requiring that the defendant be competent to stand trial during criminal proceedings include:

    1. It makes the trial go faster.
    2. It preserves the integrity of the legal system.
    3. It makes the defense attorney's job easier.
    4. It helps to ensure a fair trial.

    A. 1 & 3
    B. **2 & 4**
    C. 1, 2, & 3
    D. All of the above

42. True statements about the psychotherapist–patient privilege include:

1. Unlike confidentiality, the patient must raise the privilege to keep the physician from testifying.
2. A treating clinician might be required to testify concerning otherwise-confidential information about his or her patient if the patient asks the clinician to do so (express waiver).
3. A treating clinician might be required to testify concerning otherwise-confidential information about his or her patient if the patient has put his mental state in issue as part of the legal proceedings (implied waiver).
4. The treating clinician believes it is in the patient's best interests.

   A. 1 & 2
   B. 2 & 4
   C. **1, 2, & 3**
   D. All of the above

43. Which of the following are elements of a malpractice claim?

1. Departure from the standard of care
2. Existence of a duty of care
3. Direct or proximate causation
4. Damages

   A. 1 & 3
   B. 2 & 4
   C. 1, 2, & 3
   D. **All of the above**

44. Sexual relations with a patient can result in which of the following?

1. Suspension or loss of the psychiatrist's medical license
2. Ethical censure
3. A malpractice claim
4. Criminal conviction

   A. 1 & 3
   B. 2 & 4
   C. 1, 2, & 3
   D. **All of the above**

45. True or False. Dereliction of duty can be established either by showing that the treating clinician departed from (or ignored) the standard of care or by establishing that the treating clinician followed the standard of care but did so in an inept fashion.

A. **True**

B. False

46. True or False. The general duty of physicians is to possess and employ such reasonable skill and care as are commonly had and are exercised by respectable, average physicians in the same or similar community.

A. **True**

B. False

47. True or False. A physician who holds him or herself out as an expert in a specific area will be judged according to this higher standard, regardless of the actual credentials.

A. **True**

B. False

48. True or False. In a malpractice case, the plaintiff does not need to prove that there are damages; it is sufficient to show that there was a negligent performance of a duty.

A. True

B. **False**

49. True or False. Abandonment, in malpractice cases, can be either intentional (e.g., the doctor decides that he or she no longer wants to see a patient), or unintentional (e.g., while planning to do so, the doctor forgets to arrange for cover during vacation).

A. **True**

B. False

50. True or False. Abandonment is defined as the unilateral termination of the doctor-patient relationship, by the patient, without consent or justification, in which the termination results in harm to the patient.

A. True

B. **False**

Selected References

Informed Consent, Capacity Assessment, Treatment Refusal, and Civil Commitment

1. Appelbaum PS, Grisso T: Assessing patients' capacities to consent to treatment. *N Engl J Med.* 1988; 319: 1635–1638.

2. Appelbaum PS, Lidz CW, Meisel A: *Informed Consent: Legal Theory and Clinical Practice.* New York, Oxford University Press, 1987.

3. Appelbaum PS: Assessment of patients' competence to consent to treatment. *N Engl J Med.* 2007; 357: 1834–1840.

4. Grisso T, Appelbaum PS: *Assessing Competence to Consent to Treatment.* New York, Oxford University Press, 1998.

5. Grisso T: *Evaluating Competencies, 2nd ed.* New York: Kluwer Academic/Plenum; 2003.

6. Gutheil TG, Appelbaum PS: *Clinical Handbook of Psychiatry and the Law,* 3rd ed. Philadelphia: Lippincott Williams & Wilkins, 2000.

7. National Conference of Commisioners on Uniform State Laws: Uniform Adult Guardianship and Protective Proceedings Act. Chicago, IL: Uniform Law Commission; 2007.

8. Winick BJ: *The Right to Refuse Mental Health Treatment.* Washington, D.C., American Psychological Association, 1997.

Criminal Issues and the Role of Psychiatrists in the Legal System

1.   Almanzor MC: The effect of intoxication as a "mitigating factor" for murder and manslaughter. 31 *New Eng L Rev*. 1079; 1997.

2.   American Medical Association Council on Ethical and Judicial Affairs: *Code of Medical Ethics*, Annotation 2.06. Chicago: 1997.

3.   Drogin EY, Dattilio FM, Sadoff RL, et al. (eds): *Handbook of Forensic Assessment: Psychological and Psychiatric Perspectives*. Hoboken, NJ: John Wiley & Sons; 2011.

4.   Levine AM: Denying the settled insanity defense: another necessary step in dealing with drug and alcohol abuse. *78 B.U.L. Rev*. 75; 1998.

5.   Moore MS: *Law and Psychiatry: Rethinking the Relationship*. Cambridge: Cambridge University Press, 1984.

6.   Perlin ML: "The borderline which separated you from me": the insanity defense, the authoritarian spirit, the fear of faking, and the culture of punishment. *82 Iowa L. Rev*. 1375; 1997.

7.   Reider L: Toward a new test for the insanity defense: incorporating the discoveries of neuroscience into moral and legal theories. *46 UCLA L. Rev*. 289; 1998.

8.   Schouten R: The psychotherapist-patient privilege. *Harv Rev Psychiatry* 1998; 6: 44-48.

9.   Strasburger LH, Gutheil TG, Brodsky A: On wearing two hats: Role conflict in serving as both psychotherapist and expert witness. *Am J Psychiatry* 1997; 154: 448-456.

10.   Thomason SC: Criminal procedure-crazy as I need to be: The United States Supreme Court's latest addition to the incompetency doctrine. *20 U. Ark. Little Rock L.J.* 1998; 349.

Selected Boundary Issues

1. Bloom JD, Notman MT, Nadelson CC (eds): *Physician Sexual Misconduct.* Washington, DC: American Psychiatric Press, Inc. 1999.

2. Brendel RW, Schouten R: Legal concerns in psychosomatic medicine. Psychiatric Clin North Am. 2007; 40(4): 663–676.

3. Drogin EY, Dattilio FM, Sadoff RL, et al. (eds): *Handbook of Forensic Assessment: Psychological and Psychiatric Perspectives.* Hoboken, NJ: John Wiley & Sons; 2011.

4. Johnson RS, Persad G, Sisti D: The Tarasoff rule: the implications of interstate variation and gaps in professional training. J Am Acad Psychiatry Law. 2014; 42: 469-477.

5. *Prosser and Keeton on Torts, 5th ed.* St. Paul, West Publishing, 1984.

6. Simon RI: *Clinical Psychiatry and the Law.* Washington, APA Press, 1987.

7. Wynia MK, Papadakis MA, Sullivan WM, Hafferty FW: More than a list of values and desired behaviors: A foundational understanding of medical professionalism. *Acad Med.* 2014; 8 (5): 712-714.

About the Authors

Theodore A. Stern, MD is the Ned H. Cassem Professor of Psychiatry in the field of Psychosomatic Medicine/Consultation, Harvard Medical School and Chief Emeritus of the Avery D. Weisman Psychiatry Consultation Service, the Director of the Thomas P. Hackett Center for Scholarship in Psychosomatic Medicine, and the Director of the Office for Clinical Careers at the Massachusetts General Hospital in Boston, Massachusetts. Dr. Stern has written more than 450 scientific articles and book chapters and edited more than 25 books. These include: *Massachusetts General Hospital Handbook of General Hospital Psychiatry* (4/e–7/e); *Massachusetts General Hospital Comprehensive Clinical Psychiatry* (1/e, 2/e); *Massachusetts General Hospital Guide to Primary Care Psychiatry* (1/e, 2/e); *Massachusetts General Hospital Psychiatry Update & Board Preparations* (1/e–4/e); *Facing Cancer*; *Facing Heart Disease*; *Facing Diabetes*; *Facing Immunotherapy*; *Facing Scleroderma*; *Facing Lupus*; *Facing Osteoporosis*; *Facing Rheumatoid Arthritis*; *Facing Cystic Fibrosis*; *Facing Psoriasis*; and *Facing Overweight and Obesity*; *Learning About the Assessment and Management of Suicide Risk*; *Learning About Factitious Illness and Malingering*; *Learning About Catatonia, Neuroleptic Malignant Syndrome, and Serotonin Syndrome*; *Learning About Sleep and Sleep Disorders*; and *Learning About Agitation, Confusion, and Altered Mental Status*. He is also the editor-in-chief of *Psychosomatics*.

Ronald Schouten, MD, JD, is the Director of the Law & Psychiatry Service at Massachusetts General Hospital and an Associate Professor of Psychiatry at Harvard Medical School. He is board certified in psychiatry and forensic psychiatry and has extensive experience as a teacher and consultant in forensic psychiatry, as well as special expertise in the areas of threat assessment, violence in the workplace, the Americans with Disabilities Act, impaired professionals, and sexual harassment. Dr. Schouten has played a key role in the development of several innovations in the teaching of forensic mental health issues. He co-developed and co-taught the Managing Workplace Conflicts Program for the Massachusetts Medical Society, served on consensus panels drafting guidelines on workplace violence for the FBI and the American Society for Industrial Security, and is Forensic Column Co-Editor for the *Harvard Review of Psychiatry*. Dr. Schouten is the Immediate Past President of the New England Chapter of the Association of Threat Assessment Professionals (ATAP) and now chairs ATAP's Legislative Affairs Committee. He is the co-author of "*Almost a Psychopath: Do I (or Does Someone I Know) Have a Problem with Manipulation and Lack of Empathy*" (Hazelden/Harvard Health Publications, 2012) and edited "*Mental Health Practice and the Law*" (Oxford University Press, 2017.)